STUDIES IN MODERN ALGEBRA

Studies in Mathematics

The Mathematical Association of America

Charles W. Curtis, editor

Volume 1: STUDIES IN MODERN ANALYSIS
edited by R. C. Buck

Volume 2: STUDIES IN MODERN ALGEBRA
edited by A. A. Albert

Saunders MacLane
University of Chicago

R. H. Bruck
University of Wisconsin

Charles W. Curtis
University of Wisconsin

Erwin Kleinfeld
Syracuse University

Lowell J. Paige
University of California, Los Angeles

Studies in Mathematics

Volume 2
STUDIES IN MODERN ALGEBRA

A. A. Albert, editor
University of Chicago

Published by
The Mathematical Association of America

Distributed by
Prentice-Hall, Inc.

© *1963 by*
The Mathematical Association of America (Incorporated)
Library of Congress Catalog Card Number 63-12777

Printed in the United States of America
Prentice-Hall, Inc., Englewood Cliffs, N. J.
54131C

CONTENTS

INTRODUCTION

A. A. Albert

The six articles in this book have been chosen to present the broad aspects of modern algebraic thought. The first two, by Saunders MacLane, are survey articles, devoted almost entirely to topics of associative algebra. The remaining four present various aspects of the theory of algebraic systems with a nonassociative operation. Modern *lattice theory* and the *theory of finite planes* are not considered here, and are left to later volumes of this series.

On the basis of the first article published in the *American Mathematical Monthly* (January 1939), MacLane was awarded the Association's Chauvenet Prize.

Written as a report on a conference on algebra organized by MacLane and myself and held at the University of Chicago in 1938, its main function was to bring into sharp focus the algebraic concepts and interconnections that underlay the various topics presented at the conference and that were and are fundamental in algebraic thought. It presents the use of rings and valuations in algebraic function theory and local class field theory, the structure theory for associative algebras, and the theory of integers for

1

rational division algebras. My colloquium volume on the *Structure of Algebras* appeared eight months after the publication of this article and is a possible source for additional material for the reader.

MacLane's second survey article, written in 1961 for this volume, presents an account of recent progress in the theory of finite groups. Group theory is a very old subject, with many problems of long standing that have presented great technical difficulties. The article includes the amazing recent accomplishments in the field that have provided the machinery for additional major advances. Indeed, MacLane's article was followed by an achievement of the first magnitude by John Thompson and Walter Feit, who have now proved that *all groups of odd order are solvable*.

The article next presents the elements of the theory of modules (i.e., additive abelian groups) over commutative rings. These are algebraic systems, called $\Re$-modules, satisfying the usual postulates for a vector space, but with the scalars in a commutative ring $\Re$ rather than in a field. The elements of the theory of homomorphisms and tensor products for $\Re$-modules and the subject of categories are introduced, providing the basis for a discussion of the elementary aspects of homological algebra. This result is a purely algebraic subject, interesting and important for its own sake, but which arose as algebraic machinery useful in algebraic topology.

Homological algebra is a basic tool for the study of what are called *local rings*. These are commutative rings $\Re$ in which every ideal is finitely spanned, and which are such that the subset of all elements not having inverses in the ring (i.e., the nonunits) is an ideal of $\Re$. This concept was first introduced by Krull in 1938. A subclass of rings, *regular* local rings, is important in the study of algebraic varieties in algebraic geometry, and homological algebra actually is of major use in the study of these rings. Thus we find an algebraic tool actually developed for topological reasons to be important to the study of algebraic systems in algebraic geometry.

The remaining major topic of this article is that of *Hopf algebras* and *coalgebras*. A Hopf algebra is an associative ring that is also a module over a commutative ring $\Re$. There is also a dual ring called a coalgebra. Such algebras are of importance in topological investigations, but the postulates seem to have yielded no structure theory as yet.

In the first of the four papers on nonassociative systems, R. H. Bruck discusses systems with a single operation. He considers mathematical systems $(\mathfrak{G}, \cdot)$ consisting of a set $\mathfrak{G}$ of elements $a, b, \cdots$ and a product operation $a \cdot b = c$, such that, if any two of the elements a, b, c are given in $\mathfrak{G}$, the remaining element is a uniquely determined element of $\mathfrak{G}$. Such a system is called a *quasigroup*. If there is also an identity element e such that $e \cdot a = a \cdot e = a$ for every a of $\mathfrak{G}$, the system is called a *loop*. Bruck introduces the related topic of *Steiner triple systems* and then proceeds to the topic of *latin squares*, which are actually tables that present the results of multiplication of the elements of a finite quasigroup. He also explains the connection between quasigroups and *geometric nets* and discusses the special case of affine planes.

Bruck presents the notion of a *loop with the inverse property* and connects this property with a property of the geometric objects called *nets*. *Moufang loops* and loops satisfying other types of "inverse" laws are also described. In the section on nonassociative integers, the axioms for *neofields* are introduced and connected with a concept of exponent for powers of an element in a loop where multiplication of powers of an element *is not* associative. The exposition ends with a presentation of what are called *Room designs* in statistics and suggestions for additional reading. There is also an appendix to provide a proof of the theorem on the existence of Steiner triple systems of order n for each integer $n \geq 3$ such that n is congruent to one or three modulo 6.

The remaining three articles are concerned with nonassociative rings and algebras. It will be convenient to preface our discussion of these articles by a brief discussion of the subject as a whole. Consider a mathematical system $(\mathfrak{A}, +, \cdot)$ satisfying the postulates for a ring as given, for example, in the second MacLane article, but with the postulate that multiplication is associative *omitted*. If the system is also a vector space over a field $\mathfrak{F}$ (i.e., an $\mathfrak{F}$-module), we call it an *algebra*. It is customary to refer to the ring $\mathfrak{A}$ or the algebra $\mathfrak{A}$, where we really mean the system $(\mathfrak{A}, +, \cdot)$.

A ring $\mathfrak{A}$ is called a *division ring* if the mathematical system consisting of the set $\mathfrak{A}^*$ of all nonzero elements of $\mathfrak{A}$ and the product operation of $\mathfrak{A}$ is a loop. We say that an algebra $\mathfrak{A}$ has *degree two* over $\mathfrak{F}$ if $\mathfrak{A}$ has a unity element e (an identity element for the product operation) and every element a in $\mathfrak{A}$ is a root of an equation

$$\phi(\lambda; a) = \lambda^2 + t(a)\lambda + f(a)e,$$

where $t(a)$ is a linear form in the coordinates of $\mathfrak{A}$ and $f(a)$ is a quadratic form in these coordinates. We say that $\mathfrak{A}$ is *involutorial* over $\mathfrak{F}$ if there is a nonsingular linear transformation over $\mathfrak{F}$ (called a conjugate operation, and designated by the mapping $a \longrightarrow \bar{a}$ such that $\overline{ab} = \bar{b}\,\bar{a}$ and $\bar{\bar{a}} = a$. Finally, we call a nonassociative ring $\mathfrak{A}$ an *alternative* ring if the relations

(1) $x(xy) = (xx)y, \qquad (yx)x = y(xx)$

are valid for every x and y of $\mathfrak{A}$.

We shall be interested mainly in what are called *composition* algebras. These are involutorial alternative algebras of degree two over $\mathfrak{F}$ in which every element a has the property that $a + \bar{a} = \alpha e$ and $a\bar{a} = \bar{a}a = \beta e$, for α and β in $\mathfrak{F}$. Then

$$(\lambda - a)(\lambda - \bar{a}) = \lambda^2 - \alpha\lambda + \beta e$$

is the quadratic equation satisfied by a. Such algebras are easily constructed as follows. We begin with a composition algebra $\mathfrak{G}$ of dimension n over a field $\mathfrak{F}$ and imbed $\mathfrak{G}$ in a vector space $\mathfrak{H}$ of dimension $2n$ over $\mathfrak{F}$ whose elements are denoted by $a + bw$ for a and b in $\mathfrak{G}$. We define multiplication in $\mathfrak{H}$ by

(2) $(a + bw)(c + dw) = ac + \bar{d}b\tau + (da + b\bar{c})w$

for every a, b, c, d in $\mathfrak{G}$, where τ is a nonzero element of $\mathfrak{F}$. We also define a conjugate operation for $\mathfrak{H}$ in terms of that for $\mathfrak{G}$ by

(3) $\overline{a + bw} = \bar{a} - bw.$

If $\mathfrak{G} = e\mathfrak{F}$ is the one-dimensional algebra over $\mathfrak{F}$, it has e as unity element and is isomorphic to $\mathfrak{F}$. Then $\mathfrak{H}$ has a basis consisting of two elements e and u, with $u^2 = \lambda e \neq 0$ in $\mathfrak{F}e$, and is both associative and commutative. If we use this algebra as $\mathfrak{G}$, the new $\mathfrak{H}$

has dimension 4 and is associative but not commutative. Indeed, $\mathfrak{H}$ has basal elements e, u, v, $uv = -vu$, where $u^2 = \lambda e \neq 0$ and $v^2 = \mu e \neq 0$. It is easy to verify that the four-dimensional $\mathfrak{G}$ yields an eight-dimensional $\mathfrak{H}$, where $\mathfrak{H}$ now has a basis consisting of e, u, v, uv, w, uw, vw, $(uv)w = -u(vw)$, and is not associative. The verification that (1) holds is easily performed as follows. Since $x + \bar{x} = \alpha e$, our relations are equivalent to

$$(4) \qquad x(\bar{x}y) = (x\bar{x})y, \qquad (\bar{y}x)\bar{x} = \bar{y}(x\bar{x}).$$

We first verify that (3) does define a conjugate operation for $\mathfrak{A}$, and that

$$(a + bw)(\bar{a} - bw) = a\bar{a} - \gamma b\bar{b}$$

and

$$(a + bw) + (\bar{a} - bw) = a + \bar{a}$$

are in $\mathfrak{F}e$. Then the second relation of (4) follows from the first by conjugation. The first follows readily from (2). The construction does not stop with $n = 8$ but the system of dimension 16 is not alternative.

We are now able to discuss the last three papers. The first, by Charles W. Curtis, presents the history of the theorem on quadratic forms permitting composition in the case of division algebras. Let $\mathfrak{F}$ be any field of characteristic not two—that is, a field in which the unity element has the property that $1 + 1 \neq 0$. Every quadratic form with coefficients in $\mathfrak{F}$ can then be written as the vector and matrix product

$$(5) \qquad f(x) = xAx',$$

where $x = (x_1, \cdots, x_n)$ has independent indeterminates $x_1, \cdots, x_n$ over $\mathfrak{F}$ as coordinates and A is a nonsingular symmetric matrix with elements in $\mathfrak{F}$. Let $y = (y_1, \cdots, y_n)$ for independent indeterminates $y_1, \cdots, y_n$ over $\mathfrak{F}$, so that $f(y) = yAy'$. Then $f(x)$ is said to *permit composition* if

$$(6) \qquad f(x)f(y) = f(z),$$

where

$$(7) \qquad z = (z_1, \cdots, z_n), \qquad z_k = \sum_{i,j=1}^{n} x_i \gamma_{ijk} y_j$$

and the n^3 elements γ_{ijk} are in $\mathfrak{F}$. We may regard x and y as representing general elements in an n-dimensional vector space $\mathfrak{L}$ over $\mathfrak{F}$, and (7) then defines a product operation $x \cdot y = z$ for an algebra $\mathfrak{A}_0 = (\mathfrak{L}, \cdot)$ over $\mathfrak{F}$. The quadratic form $f(x)$ can be normalized so that its matrix A is a diagonal matrix and so

(8) $f(x) = \alpha_1 x_1^2 + \cdots + \alpha_n x_n^2 \qquad (\alpha_i \neq 0 \text{ in } \mathfrak{F}).$

It can be shown that it is always possible to take $\alpha_1 = 1$ when (6) holds. Then there is a so-called *isotopic* algebra $\mathfrak{A}$ with $e = (1, 0, \cdots, 0)$ as unity element, which also has the property of (6) where $z = x \cdot y$, and $x \cdot y$ is the product in the new algebra $\mathfrak{A}$.

The problem in the theory of quadratic forms being considered is that of finding necessary and sufficient conditions that a quadratic form permit composition. The answer is that the form $f(x)$ shall be the product $x\bar{x}$ in the algebra $\mathfrak{A}$ and that $\mathfrak{A}$ must be one of our composition algebras of dimension $1, 2, 4$, or 8. In his article, Curtis emphasizes the case where $f(x) = x_1^2 + \cdots + x_n^2$ and $\mathfrak{F}$ is the field of all real numbers. Then $\mathfrak{A}$ is this field when $n = 1$, is the field of complex numbers when $n = 2$, the noncommutative Hamilton algebra of real quaternions when $n = 4$, and the algebra of order 8 discovered by A. Cayley in 1845. In each of these cases the algebras are division algebras, and in fact the product $x\bar{x}$ is a norm and is not zero for $x \neq 0$. The original stimulus for inventing these algebras was an attempt to generalize the notion of a real field. The extension to complex numbers resulted in the loss of order, but the existence of the norm compensated for this to some extent. The extension to a four-dimensional system resulted in the loss of commutativity, and the extension to dimension 8 in the loss of associativity.

The paper by Kleinfeld has its origin to some extent in the colloquium lectures given by M. H. Stone in 1939. In those Madison Lectures, Stone presented a theory of convexity and stated that the mathematical system needed for the theory was an ordered alternative ring. Infinite-dimensional associative ordered rings are known, and in one lecture Stone raised the question of the existence of ordered nonassociative but alternative rings. Kleinfeld's

article presents his and Bruck's famous proof of the theorem that
every alternative division ring is either associative or is an eight-
dimensional Cayley algebra. As a real Cayley algebra contains
an unordered quaternion algebra, the whole algebra cannot be
ordered, and this then yields a negative answer to Stone's question.

The final article is an exposition of the theory of Jordan algebras
by Lowell J. Paige. It begins with some general properties of nonassociative algebras including the concept of radical, simple, and
semisimple algebras, and goes on to present the process of con-
structing Lie and Jordan algebras from appropriately closed subspaces of associative algebras. These Jordan algebras are called
special. Paige also discusses the structure theory of Jordan algebras of characteristic zero, as obtained by using a trace argument,
which is strongly connected with the paper of Curtis for the following reason. If the field $\mathfrak{F}$ is algebraically closed, every simple
Jordan algebra $\mathfrak{H}$ over $\mathfrak{F}$ has a unity element e that can be expressed as a sum $e = e_1 + \cdots + e_t$ of idempotents e_i such that
$e_i e_j = 0$ for $i \neq j$, and no e_i is a sum $e_i = f_i + g_i$ for idempotents
f_i and g_i whose product is zero. Then t is a unique integer called
the *degree* of $\mathfrak{H}$ over $\mathfrak{F}$. When $t > 2$ it can be shown that $\mathfrak{H}$ is
actually the set $\mathfrak{H}_t(C)$ of all t-rowed Hermitian matrices $B = \overline{B}'$
with elements in a composition algebra $\mathfrak{C}$. Conversely, every such
$\mathfrak{H}$ is a simple Jordan algebra providing that when $t > 3$ the algebra $\mathfrak{C}$ must be associative.

The article also contains some remarks on *free associative algebras, free Jordan algebras*, and an outline of the proof of the
Albert-Paige theorem, which states that if $\mathfrak{C}$ is the Cayley algebra,
the *exceptional* Jordan algebra $\mathfrak{H}_3(\mathfrak{C})$ is not the homomorphic
image of any special Jordan algebra. The article concludes with
some remarks on unsolved problems.

As indicated in the article by Paige, the theory of Jordan algebras
is of major importance in the study of Lie algebras. Moreover,
this portion of the theory is strongly connected with the excep-
tional Jordan algebra $\mathfrak{H}_3(\mathfrak{C})$, and hence with the Cayley algebra of
the paper by Curtis, which has been shown by Kleinfeld to be the
only simple alternative ring that is not associative. Thus, our

final three papers again demonstrate the strong interconnections among various topics in algebra and, through the connection with Lie algebras, connections with Lie groups and thus with other branches of mathematics.

SOME RECENT ADVANCES IN ALGEBRA

Saunders MacLane

The rapid exploitation of the new techniques of abstract algebra
and the introduction of many new types of algebraic systems,
though perhaps superficially confusing, have actually centered
about several well-defined lines of investigation: function fields,
linear algebras, p-adic fields, Lie algebras, matrices. The present
direction and the close interrelation of these fields of investigation
were clearly indicated in a conference on algebra held at the University of Chicago. We here attempt to summarize some of the
ideas and interconnections brought out at this conference, not in
the fashion of a handbook or monograph, but rather as a survey
for the generally interested mathematical public. After the necessary background has been filled in, we state the sorts of problems
considered and the types of answers obtained. For detailed statements of results we refer to the skeleton bibliography at the end.
In the last Section (12) we attempt to state a general definition of
algebra and a summary of its fundamental problems. To the
authors whose ideas are here assembled, we apologize for the
omission, inevitably attendant upon such a summary, of the many
difficulties and subtleties of their work.

1. ALGEBRAIC GEOMETRY, POWER SERIES
AND VALUATIONS

The relation of algebra to algebraic geometry was a lively topic of debate, stimulated by a paper of Lefschetz on the use of formal power series in algebraic geometry [21]. The origin of this algebraic-geometric connection might be described thus: the geometry of an algebraic curve can be reduced to the algebra of a certain corresponding field;† specifically, if k denotes the field of all complex numbers, and if a curve is defined in the plane by an irreducible polynomial equation $f(x, y) = 0$, then the corresponding field K is the totality $k(x, y)$ of all rational functions $z = g(x, y)/h(x, y)$ with complex coefficients of the two quantities x and y. It should be emphasized that x and y do not figure in this field as variables taking on values in the sense of analysis, but merely as quantities on which rational operations of addition, multiplication, etc., can be performed, subject always to the proviso that the rational combination $f(x, y)$ be 0. The use of this "function field" $k(x, y)$ corresponding to the curve has one considerable advantage: a birational transformation of the curve will leave the corresponding field invariant.

Near a point $x = a$, $y = b$ of the curve $f(x, y) = 0$, the variable y can be expanded in one or more series of the form

$$(1) \qquad y = b + b_1t + b_2t^2 + \cdots, \qquad t = (x - a)^{1/n},$$

when t is a suitably chosen integral or fractional power of $x - a$. This series (1), the Puiseux expansion, is usually treated as a convergent series defining an element or "cycle" of the algebraic function y of x, but Lefschetz emphasizes the purely formal character of this expansion. The central fact is that the Puiseux series (1), if substituted in $f(x, y)$, yields an identity $f(x, y) \equiv 0$ in t. Conversely, any series (1) which formally satisfies the equation $f = 0$ is the Puiseux series corresponding to some branch of the algebraic curve, or, alternatively, determines a corresponding point P on the

---

† For the definitions of a few fundamental algebraic terms (group, field, and the like), one may refer to the glossary in Albert [1].

Riemann surface of the algebraic function $y(x)$. Any rational function $z = R(x, y)$ in the field $K = k(x, y)$ becomes a power series in t after substitution of the series for y and that for x, $x = a + t^n$:

$$(2) \qquad\qquad z = t^{\nu}(a_0 + a_1 t + a_2 t^2 + \cdots),$$

where the integer ν may be positive, negative, or zero, and the a_i are in the coefficient field k of all complex numbers. The set of all such possible power series forms a field $k\{t\}$, because such series can be added, divided, and multiplied by the usual formal procedures. The point P determined by (1) on the Riemann surface can be said to yield a one-to-one map (2) of the functions z of the field K onto a subset of the power series field $k\{t\}$, and this map is an *isomorphism* because any rational relation which holds between several functions of the field must hold between their corresponding power series.

This formal treatment by power series will apply now to algebraic curves even when the field k of constants is not the classical complex number field, but any field k which is algebraically closed, in the sense that every polynomial equation over k has a root in k—that is, for any field k in which the fundamental theorem of algebra holds. Lefschetz pointed out that on this basis most of the classical treatment of algebraic functions of one and two variables, as presented, for instance, by Picard or Weierstrass, can be developed as pure algebra. The abelian integrals and their classification can be managed algebraically in terms of abelian differentials $g(x, y)\, dx$. Moreover, the genus of an algebraic curve, an important invariant often defined topologically as the number of holes in the Riemann surface (a pretzel), can be defined algebraically, in terms of these integrals, as the maximum number of linearly independent differentials of the "first kind." One or two theorems of an essentially topological character cannot be generalized, but Lefschetz conjectured that the Riemann-Roch theorem could be treated algebraically not only by the usual arithmetic proof [31], but even by one of the classical geometric proofs [21] (see §23). This formal series treatment is of utility in other parts of analysis, notably in the treatment of algebraic functions of Dirichlet series [26].

The importance of the application of algebra to geometry was

emphasized by Zariski's new proof that the singularities of an algebraic surface can be eliminated by suitable birational transformations. Previously the only sound proof of this important theorem
had been Walker's [32], using analytic functions. If the algebraic
surface S is given in three-space by a single homogeneous algebraic
equation $f(x_0, x_1, x_2, x_3) = 0$, then the singular points are those
points of the surface at which certain partial derivatives simultaneously vanish. The theorem requires that the surface S be
represented in n-space with coordinates $y_0, y_1, \cdots, y_n$ by a nonsingular surface S' which is a birational transform of the original
surface S in the sense that the y's are rational functions of the x's
and conversely. One difficulty in eliminating singular points arises
because a transformation carefully constructed to eliminate one
singular point may explode some other singular point into a whole
singular curve. Zariski treats this difficulty by repeatedly using an
"integral closure" process which gets rid of singular curves. In
terms of the nonhomogeneous coordinates $\xi_1 = x_1/x_0$, $\xi_2 = x_2/x_0$,
$\xi_3 = x_3/x_0$, a rational function $\eta = \eta(\xi_1, \xi_2, \xi_3)$ is called *integral* if it
satisfies a polynomial equation,

$$\eta^m + a_1(\xi_1, \xi_2, \xi_3)\eta^{m-1} + \cdots + a_m(\xi_1, \xi_2, \xi_3) = 0,$$

with first coefficient 1 and the other coefficients polynomials in
the ξ_i. The nonhomogeneous integral closure process is a birational
transformation replacing the coordinates ξ_1, ξ_2, ξ_3 by integral functions $\eta_1, \eta_2, \cdots, \eta_n$ chosen so that every integral function of the ξ_i
is a polynomial in these new coordinates η_j. After this process has
removed singular curves, the nature of one of the remaining
isolated singular points P depends on the sorts of curves (or
"branches") passing through P on the surface. Such a branch can
be represented algebraically by a certain corresponding "valuation." The reduction of the singularity is effected by applying to
suitable branches at P a "uniformization lemma," which expresses
the coordinates as holomorphic functions (integral power series)
of two parameters u and v—where these parameters can be chosen
as rational functions of the original coordinates (for such valuations, *cf.* Zariski [36]).

The study of valuations occurs not only in algebraic geometry but also in algebraic number theory and other arithmetical questions. If the power series expansion (2) of an algebraic function z at a point P begins with a nonvanishing term $a_0 t^\nu$, then the order or *value* $V(z)$ at P may be defined to be the exponent ν of that term.

$$(3) \qquad V(z) = \nu \quad \text{if} \quad z = a_0 t^\nu + a_1 t^{\nu+1} + \cdots \qquad (a_0 \neq 0).$$

When z has a zero at $t = 0$, $V(z)$ is the order of this zero; when z has a pole at $t = 0$, $V(z)$ is the negative of the order of the pole. This valuation for a sum or product of two functions z and w can be shown to have the properties

$$(4) \qquad V(zw) = V(z) + V(w), \qquad V(z + w) \geq \min\,(V(z),\, V(w)).$$

Any real-valued function $V(z)$ defined in a field K and having these two properties is known as a *valuation* of that field. Any such V can also be converted into an "absolute value" $||z|| = e^{-V(z)}$, with corresponding properties

$$||zw|| = ||z|| \cdot ||w||, \qquad ||z + w|| \leq \max\,(||z||,\, ||w||).$$

The second of these properties is even stronger than the usual triangle axiom $|z + w| \leq |z| + |w|$ for complex numbers. Thus $||z||$ behaves like the absolute value of z, and limits with respect to it can be defined in the usual way. Especially important are the fields K' which are *complete* with respect to an absolute value, in the sense that every sequence $a_1, a_2, \cdots$ which is a Cauchy sequence has a limit a in the field K'. For instance, the field $K' = k\{t\}$ of all formal power series (2) with $||z|| = \exp\,(-V(z))$ given by (3) is a typical complete field.

Arithmetically, any prime number p determines a valuation V_p of the integers, if $V_p(n)$ is defined as the exponent of the highest power of p dividing n,

$$(5) \qquad V_p(p^\nu b) = \nu, \qquad n = p^\nu b, \qquad b \text{ prime to } p.$$

The field R of rational numbers n/m with this "p-adic" valuation $V_p(n/m) = V_p(n) - V_p(m)$ can be embedded in a larger *p-adic number field* R_p complete with respect to V_p. The structure of this field R_p is determined by the behavior of the residues (mod p), which themselves form a field, the Galois field containing p elements $0, 1, 2, \cdots, p - 1$. Similarly, the residues (mod t) of the power series (3) form a field, the field k of coefficients. Such *residue-class fields* occur for other fields K with valuations like V. Any complete field K whose valuation function V takes on only integral values is essentially determined by its residue-class field.

Just as in the Galois theory, the structure of such a field and the form of its subfields depend upon the possible "symmetries" of the field. A symmetry of a field F is technically known as an *automorphism*: a map of the field upon itself which preserves rational relations. In other words, an *automorphism* S of F is a one-to-one correspondence $x \longleftrightarrow x^S$ of the field F to itself such that sums and products correspond to sums and products:

$$(6) \qquad (x + y)^S = x^S + y^S; \qquad (xy)^S = x^S y^S.$$

The successive application of two automorphisms S and T yields a new automorphism $x \longleftrightarrow (x^S)^T$ called the product ST. Under this product the automorphisms of F form a group. For certain complete fields like the p-adic fields this group G has been investigated by MacLane, who finds certain subgroups of G analogous to Hilbert's "inertial" and "ramification" groups for prime ideals (*cf.* also MacLane [24]).

2. THE LATTICE REPRESENTATION OF THE STRUCTURE OF GROUPS

Recent algebraic investigations have shown that the structure of a group depends vitally upon the number and arrangement of its subgroups. An instance in point is the Jordan-Hölder theorem, which asserts that certain chains of relatively normal subgroups of a group must always have the same length. Two subgroups H and K of a given group can be combined in two ways, to yield the *intersection* $H \cap K$ of the two subgroups and the *union* $H \cup K$, which is the smallest subgroup containing both H and K. Relative to these two operations the subgroups are said to form a *lattice* or *structure*. A lattice can also be defined abstractly in terms of the associative and other laws satisfied by intersection and union [25, 6].

Since the lattice of subgroups represents many of the properties of a group, one comes inevitably to this question: when is the nature of the group G completely determined by its lattice of subgroups? Since G is an abstract group, its subgroup lattice L will be exactly like the subgroup lattice of any group G' *isomorphic* to G. To say that G is isomorphic to G' means that there is a one-to-one correspondence $T: A \longleftrightarrow A^T$ between the elements A of the group G and the elements $A' = A^T$ of the group G' such that products correspond to products:

(7)   If $A \longleftrightarrow A^T$, $B \longleftrightarrow B^T$, then $AB \longleftrightarrow A^T B^T$.

Under this isomorphism T each subgroup H of G goes into a subset H^τ of G' composed of all images A^T of elements A of H. This correspondence $H \longleftrightarrow H^\tau$ is a one-to-one correspondence between the subgroups of G and those of G' such that unions and intersections are preserved:

(8) $(H \cap K)^\tau = H^\tau \cap K^\tau, \qquad (H \cup K)^\tau = H^\tau \cup K^\tau.$

Conversely, a one-to-one correspondence $H \longleftrightarrow H^\tau$ between the subgroups H of G and the subgroups H' of another group G' is called a *subgroup isomorphism* of G to G' if property (8) holds. Hence arises the natural question: Are two subgroup-isomorphic groups G and G' necessarily (elementwise) isomorphic? An affirmative answer would mean that the structure of a group is actually determined by the lattice of its subgroups. The answer is not always affirmative, but Baer has an answer in the case of abelian groups. If the group is one of certain listed types, which are all "small" groups in the sense that they have relatively few subgroups, the answer is no. For other abelian groups, the answer is yes; subgroup-isomorphic groups are in fact isomorphic, and in many cases the only subgroup isomorphisms are those generated in the above fashion by ordinary isomorphisms.

3. GENERALIZED QUATERNIONS

Systems of elements subject to the rational operations of addition and multiplication but not satisfying the commutative law for multiplication were first discovered in the guise of quaternions during the last century. A real quaternion algebra Q is the set of all linear combinations Y of four basal elements 1, i, j, ij,

$$(9) \qquad Y = y_1 + y_2 i + y_3 j + y_4 ij,$$

where the components $y_1, \cdots, y_4$ are real numbers. The rational operations on such elements are: *scalar multiplication*—Y is multiplied by a real number b by multiplying each component y_i by that number b; *addition*—two elements Y and Z are added by adding corresponding components; *multiplication*—the product of two elements Y and Z is found by using the usual distributive and associative laws and the following table for the products of the four basal elements:

$$(10) \qquad i^2 = -1, \qquad j^2 = -1, \qquad ij = -ji.$$

The system Q is called a *linear associative algebra* because it is a set of elements closed with respect to these three operations and because these operations satisfy the usual algebraic laws (excluding the law $YZ = ZY$). This system Q is an algebra *over* the field of real numbers because the components are elements from that field.

Wedderburn first introduced the consideration of such linear algebras over fields other than the real number field. Over the field of rational numbers, for instance, one has quaternion algebras $Q(\alpha, \beta)$ consisting of all elements Y of (9) with rational components and a multiplication table

$$(11) \qquad i^2 = \alpha, \qquad j^2 = \beta, \qquad ij = -ji,$$

where α and β are fixed rational integers. Aside from the fact that the same algebra might be represented with different basal units i' and j' using different constants α' and β', there are infinitely many essentially different quaternion algebras $Q(\alpha, \beta)$, two algebras being the same only if a certain "fundamental number" determined by α and β is the same.† The importance and variety of the

---

† In terms of this fundamental number a certain simplified canonical form of the table (11) is possible, as shown in Albert [2] and Latimer [19].

algebras possible over the field of rational numbers and other fields were recognized by Dickson, whose researches have paved the way for the far-reaching theory of algebras over many types of fields.

The structure of an algebra depends upon the form of its subfields and subalgebras. The quaternion algebra $Q(\alpha, \beta)$ contains the set $R(\sqrt{\alpha})$ of all elements $x = y_1 + y_2 i$. This set is a field; it is obtained from the field R of rational numbers by adjoining i with $i^2 = \alpha$, for $R(\sqrt{\alpha})$ consists of all rational functions of i with coefficients in R. Each element $x = y_1 + y_2 i$ of the field $R(\sqrt{\alpha})$ has a conjugate $\bar{x} = y_1 - y_2 i$, and the correspondence $x \longleftrightarrow \bar{x}$ is a one-to-one correspondence of the field $R(\sqrt{\alpha})$ to itself. Since $\overline{x_1 x_2} = \bar{x}_1 \bar{x}_2$, $\overline{x_1 + x_2} = \bar{x}_1 + \bar{x}_2$, this correspondence preserves sums and products and hence is an automorphism of the field in the sense of (6). In terms of this subfield $R(\sqrt{\alpha})$, the general quaternion (9) can be written as

$$(12) \qquad Y = (y_1 + y_2 i) + j(y_3 - y_4 i) = x_1 + j x_2,$$

where $x_1 = y_1 + y_2 i$ and $x_2 = y_3 - y_4 i$ are elements in the field $R(\sqrt{\alpha})$. The multiplication table (11) implies that

$$x_1 j = (y_1 + y_2 i) j = y_1 j - y_2 j i = j(y_1 - y_2 i) = j \bar{x}_1,$$

and hence we can write a new table in terms of conjugates as

$$(13) \qquad j^2 = \beta, \qquad x j = j \bar{x}, \qquad \text{for } x \text{ in } R(\sqrt{\alpha}).$$

This automorphism formulation of the quaternions has latent potentialities for generalization.

4. ARITHMETICS OF QUATERNIONS

Arithmetic can be considered in an algebra if one can select in the algebra a suitable set J of integral numbers which, like the ordinary integers, form a *ring*—that is, a subset J of the algebra closed under addition, subtraction, and multiplication. In the quadratic algebraic number field $K = R(\sqrt{\alpha})$, every element $x = y_1 + y_2 \sqrt{\alpha}$ satisfies a quadratic equation

$$[t - (y_1 + y_2\sqrt{\alpha})][t - (y_1 - y_2\sqrt{\alpha})] =$$
$$t^2 - 2y_1 t + (y_1^2 - y_2^2 \alpha) = 0$$

with rational coefficients. The number x is called an *integer* if this equation has integral coefficients.† The set of all integers then forms a ring. For quaternions one could attempt the same definition, for the quaternion Y of (12) satisfies a rational equation whose roots are $Y = x_1 + jx_2$ and its conjugate $\overline{Y} = \overline{x}_1 - jx_2$,

$$(14) \qquad (t - Y)(t - \overline{Y}) = t^2 - 2y_1 t + N(Y) = 0.$$

Here the constant term $N(Y) = Y\overline{Y}$ is the so-called *norm* of Y,

$$(15) \quad N(Y) = Y\overline{Y} = (x_1 + jx_2)(\overline{x}_1 - jx_2) = x_1\overline{x}_1 - \beta x_2 x_2.$$

If the previous definition of an integer is now applied, so that Y is called integral if this equation (14) has rational integers as coefficients, then the set of integers unfortunately may no longer be a ring because there can be two integers whose sum is not integral.

As a substitute one may consider the set $\mathfrak{g}$ of all quaternions $Y = x_1 + jx_2$ for which the numbers x_1 and x_2 of the field $R(\sqrt{\alpha})$ are integers. This set is too much dependent upon the particular choice of j, but has most of the requisite properties:

(C): $\mathfrak{g}$ is a ring;

(R'): every element of $\mathfrak{g}$ satisfies a polynomial equation [for instance, the equation (14)] which has a first coefficient 1 and the remaining coefficients rational integers;

(U'): $\mathfrak{g}$ contains all the rational integers of R and contains just as many linearly independent elements over R as does the whole quaternion algebra $Q(\alpha, \beta)$.

This last property is immediate, for $\mathfrak{g}$ contains the four basal elements 1, i, j, and ij which are linearly independent by the construction of the algebra. A subset $\mathfrak{g}$ of an algebra having these three properties (C), (R'), and (U') is called an *order* of the algebra. Dickson recognized that a set of integers in more general algebras is more suitably defined as a *maximal order*‡ $\mathfrak{g}$—that is, an order which is contained in no larger order of the algebra. Every order

---

† Zariski's treatment of the singularities of surfaces involves essentially the same notion of an integer (Sec. 1).

‡ This terminology is not that used by Dickson himself. See Dickson [9].

is then contained in at least one maximal order; in particular, the ring $\mathfrak{g}$ defined above for the quaternions is not usually itself a maximal order, but can be extended so as to become one.

The arithmetic properties of a maximal order $\mathfrak{D}$ again depend upon a suitable type of subsystem of the order: the *ideals* of the order. A subset $\mathfrak{a}$ of $\mathfrak{D}$ is a *left ideal* of $\mathfrak{D}$ if the difference of two elements of $\mathfrak{a}$ is again an element of $\mathfrak{a}$, and if the product ba is in $\mathfrak{a}$ for any b in $\mathfrak{D}$ and a in $\mathfrak{a}$. One also requires that an ideal contain at least one rational integer. In particular, for any element a_0 in $\mathfrak{D}$ the set (a_0) of all elements ba_0 for b in $\mathfrak{D}$ is an ideal. This ideal is the *principal ideal* generated by a_0. Similarly, left and right ideals can be considered in any ring.

5. QUADRATIC FORMS AND QUATERNIONS

Quaternion algebras reflect many properties of quadratic and hermitian forms, because the norm of a quaternion is itself such a form. The norm $N(Y)$ as calculated in (15) is a simple hermitian form in the variables x_1 and x_2. Directly in terms of the original components $y_1, \cdots, y_4$ of (9), the norm $N(\overline{Y}) = Y\overline{Y}$ with $\overline{Y} = y_1 - y_2 i - y_3 j - y_4 ij$ becomes the quadratic form

$$N(Y) = y_1^2 - \alpha y_2^2 - \beta y_3^2 + \alpha\beta y_4^2.$$

This hermitian form interpretation has been investigated in terms of ideals by Latimer. The order $\mathfrak{g}$ of integers used above has a *basis* $1, j$, in the sense that $\mathfrak{g}$ consists of all linear combinations $x_1 + jx_2$ of 1 and j with coefficients x_1 and x_2 integers of the quadratic field $R(\sqrt{\alpha})$. Similarly, any left ideal $\mathfrak{a}$ of this ring has a basis ω_1 and ω_2, so that any element of $\mathfrak{a}$ can be expressed as $x\omega_1 + y\omega_2$ for x and y again integers of $R(\sqrt{\alpha})$. The norm of this element $x\omega_1 + y\omega_2$ is, except for a constant factor, a form

(16) $$ax\overline{x} + \overline{b}\overline{x}y + bx\overline{y} + cy\overline{y}.$$

This form is hermitian because it is equal to its own conjugate—the coefficients a and c are rational integers and the cross product terms have conjugate coefficients b and $\overline{b}$. The determinant

$b\bar{b} - ac$ of this form turns out to be the constant β used in the multiplication tables (13) and (11).

An ideal $\mathfrak{a}$ with a given basis ω_1, ω_2 then corresponds to a hermitian form of determinant β over the field $R(\sqrt{\alpha})$, and conversely. If the basis of the ideal is changed, one gets a new form equivalent to the first in the sense that it can be obtained from the first by a linear homogeneous transformation of determinant 1. The possible classes of equivalent forms can further be put into correspondence with certain classes of ideals†—where two ideals belong to the same class when they differ by principal ideal factors (with positive norms). This means that facts about the classes of forms can be translated into facts about classes of ideals. In particular, Latimer has found certain quaternion algebras with just one class of ideals. This statement means that every (regular) ideal is a principal ideal and hence that the ideal structure of the ring is as simple as possible [18, 20].

The quaternion algebras can also be used as a starting point for the treatment of properties of quadratic forms in many variables, of the type

$$f(x_1, x_2, \cdots , x_n) = \Sigma \, a_{ij}x_ix_j \qquad (i, j = 1, \cdots , n),$$

where the coefficients a_{ij} are in the field R of rational numbers and can be chosen so that $a_{ij} = a_{ji}$. Many questions of the representation of numbers by such forms lead to the "representation of zero" by numbers in any field F containing the rational field R. The form f is said to *properly represent* 0 in the field F if there are numbers $x_1, x_2, \cdots , x_n$ not all zero in the field F such that $f(x_1, \cdots , x_n) = 0$. Here F might be the field R_0 of all real numbers, which is complete with respect to the ordinary absolute value, or a p-adic number field R_p which contains R and is complete with respect to the p-adic valuations of (5), Sec. 1. If f represents 0 in the original field R, then it certainly represents 0 in any one of these larger fields R_0 and R_p. A theorem due to Hasse now states a converse: If the form $f(x_1, \cdots , x_n)$ properly represents 0 in the real number

---

† Because the ring $\mathfrak{D}$ is not a maximal order, it is necessary here to consider not all ideals but only certain "regular" ideals.

field R_0 and in every p-adic field R_p, then it also properly represents 0 in the field of rationals [34, 11]. This type of theorem, which starts from the behavior "locally" for each prime p and derives the behavior in the original field R, has attracted much current interest (see also the class field theory discussed in Sec. 11). Artin has now a new and elegant proof for this theorem of Hasse, using an induction on the number of variables combined with a treatment of the four-variable case in terms of the norm forms of quaternion algebras. His proof also applies when R is replaced by an algebraic number field.

6. THE STRUCTURE OF ALGEBRAS

We turn now to the general definition of a linear associative algebra over an arbitrary field F. An algebra A consists of all linear combinations

$$(17) \qquad a = \alpha_1 u_1 + \cdots + \alpha_n u_n = \Sigma \, \alpha_i u_i$$

of n basal elements $u_1, \cdots, u_n$ with coefficients α_i in the field F. The sum of two such elements is given by

$$(18) \quad (\Sigma \, \alpha_i u_i) + (\Sigma \, \beta_i u_i) = \Sigma \, (\alpha_i + \beta_i) u_i \qquad (i = 1, \cdots, n),$$

and the scalar product of an element a by an element β of the field F is determined by

$$(19) \qquad \beta(\Sigma \, \alpha_i u_i) = \Sigma \, (\beta \alpha_i) u_i \qquad (i = 1, \cdots, n).$$

The product of two elements a and b in the algebra is defined by the formula

$$(20) \quad (\Sigma \, \alpha_i u_i)(\Sigma \, \beta_j u_j) = \Sigma \, (\alpha_i \beta_j) u_i u_j \qquad (i, j, = 1, \cdots, n),$$

which is completed by a table giving the product $u_i u_j$ of each pair of basal elements as some particular element of the algebra. This multiplication table must be such that the product $a \cdot b$ satisfies the associative law. The number n of basal elements of the algebra A is its *order*; it can be characterized by the statement that the n basal elements are linearly independent, whereas any $n + 1$ elements of A are necessarily linearly dependent.

We shall assume that the algebra A has a unit element 1 with the property that $1 \cdot a = a \cdot 1 = a$ for every a of the algebra—for if there were no such element we could construct it and add it to the algebra. The algebra then contains the elements $1 \cdot \alpha$ which behave like the corresponding α's of the field F and thus can be identified with the elements of F, so that the algebra then contains its coefficient field F.

Certain types of algebras are important. A *division algebra* is an algebra in which every $a \neq 0$ has an inverse a^{-1} such that $a^{-1}a = aa^{-1} = 1$. An algebra is *simple* if it contains no proper subset which is a two-sided ideal (both a left and a right ideal, as at the end of Sec. 4). Such algebras exist: any division algebra is necessarily simple in this sense. A simple algebra is *normal* (or, equivalently, *central*) if it is as uncommutative as possible: that is, if b is an element of the algebra such that $bx = xb$ is true for every x, then b is necessarily an element $b = \beta$ of the coefficient field F.

A major problem in the study of linear algebras is the construction of all algebras out of fields or out of simpler algebras in systematic fashion. The object of such investigations is then a more concrete representation for algebras than that given by the general definition. Matrices yield algebras; for the set of all $m \times m$ square matrices with elements in a field F is an algebra M_m (a so-called *total matrix algebra*). The m^2 matrices with 1 in one position and 0 elsewhere can be considered as its $n = m^2$ basal elements $u_1, \cdots , u_n$. This matrix construction can be generalized if we consider the set of all $m \times m$ matrices with the usual matrix multiplication, but with elements themselves taken from a given normal division algebra D over the field F. The algebras which can be obtained in this fashion are all the normal simple algebras; they are the important type because all other algebras can be decomposed into such normal simple ones by certain structure theorems of Wedderburn [33, chap. 10].

New algebras can be formed by combinations of old ones. If A and B are two algebras over a field F, one can construct a new algebra, the direct product $A \times B$, which contains both the given algebras A and B. Specifically, $A \times B$ consists of all sums

$$(21) \qquad c = b_1 u_1 + \cdots + b_n u_n$$

Such a diagonal matrix, which has zeros everywhere but on the main diagonal, may be represented by simply writing down the diagonal elements $\{z_1, \cdots, z_t\}$. The automorphism S of the field then generates an automorphism of these matrices which may be obtained by permuting the diagonal elements cyclicly and then applying S to the last element

$$\{z_1, \cdots, z_t\} \longleftrightarrow \{z_2, \cdots, z_t, z_1^S\}.$$

Relative to this correspondence the semi-fields behave very much like ordinary cyclic fields.

An outstanding problem concerns the nature of normal division algebras and normal simple algebras over general fields F—where there might be division algebras which are not cyclic algebras. The cyclic algebras $A = (Z, S, \gamma)$ [$cf.$ (23)] are characterized by the fact that they contain a cyclic subfield Z which is maximal (contained in no larger subfield). Any normal division algebra over F still contains a maximal subfield K—but this subfield may have too few automorphisms to be normal† or may not have a cyclic automorphism group. The multiplication table in the algebra may still be described by a more complicated multiplication table depending on certain automorphisms after the fashion of (23). The structure of such algebras has been analyzed by Brauer [7] who makes considerable use of two tools: first, any algebra A over F can be extended to a larger algebra A_K over a given field K containing F—one need only consider the element (17) of the algebra with the same basal units, but now with coefficients α_i taken from the larger field K; second, any algebra A can be considered as an algebra of certain matrices with components in F, for any element a of the algebra has certain products with the basal elements,

$$(24) \qquad au_i = \alpha_{i1}u_1 + \cdots + \alpha_{in}u_n.$$

The correspondence between the element a and the matrix $a^* = (\alpha_{ij})$ "represents" A as a matrix algebra. By simplifying these matrices one obtains reductions of this representation to

---

† A field K over F is *normal* if it is obtained by adjoining to F *all* roots of an equation; a normal field of degree n over F usually has n automorphisms over F.

certain irreducible representations over F or K; their construction
by Brauer yields information about the algebra.

8. ARITHMETIC OF CYCLIC ALGEBRAS

The arithmetic study of a general algebra can be reduced to the
study of the normal simple algebras. Here again the basic necessity
is the definition of a set of integers—and such sets are defined as
maximal orders in exactly the fashion discussed above (Sec. 4) for
the quaternion algebras. But the definition of such sets and the
description of their properties is not the only problem. How can
these maximal orders be explicitly found in the case of particular
algebras, say for cyclic algebras? How many such orders are there?
Some answers have been found for the special case when the cyclic
algebra is a quaternion algebra, and Hull has extended the method
to any cyclic algebra generated over the field of rational numbers
by a cyclic field Z of odd prime degree. Such a cyclic algebra might
be represented in several different ways by the generation (Z, S, γ)
of (22) and (23), but there is a certain canonical generation which
is found by considering the algebra not over the rational number
field, but over the larger p-adic number fields constructed in Sec. 1,
from the valuation (5) belonging to a rational prime p. In this
generation one might naturally define an integer to be an element
(22) of the algebra in which the coefficients z_i are integers of the
algebraic number field Z. This set of integers is an order, but not
a maximal order, and Hull [12] finds that it can be embedded in
exactly n distinct maximal orders which can be explicitly represented in terms of the solutions of certain congruences. All other
maximal orders can be obtained from any one of these. This
method of finding formulas for maximal orders is a fruitful one,
for it has been extended by Perlis [27] to the case of cyclic algebras
over the rationals where the degree of the cyclic field is not a prime
but a power of a prime.

In any maximal order $\mathfrak{D}$ the study of arithmetic questions of
divisibility leads inevitably to the study of the divisors of 1. Such
numbers, called *units* of $\mathfrak{D}$, are simply the elements $a \neq 0$ in $\mathfrak{D}$

which have reciprocals $1/a$ also in the order $\mathfrak{D}$. These units form a group under multiplication. Recently [10] advances have been made in studying the totality of units and the structure of the group which they form; the typical theorem gives an expression of the units in terms of a finite set of "fundamental" units. Hull has successfully applied these methods to the orders of quaternion algebras, where the group G can be represented geometrically as a certain Fuchsian group.

The ideal theory in a maximal order of a normal simple algebra (we recall that such algebras include the cyclic algebras) has been developed extensively. MacDuffee [23] has shown that many of the requisite computations with ideals can be carried out effectively by the use of matrices. This use of matrices depends directly upon the representation of an algebra in terms of matrices, discussed above in (24). Specifically, an ideal $\mathfrak{a}$ in a maximal order $\mathfrak{D}$ of such an algebra over the rational number field always has a basis $\omega_1, \cdots, \omega_n$ such that the ideal consists of all linear combinations

$$(25) \qquad b = \beta_1\omega_1 + \cdots + \beta_n\omega_n,$$

for rational integral coefficients β_i. The elements of this basis of the ideal can be represented in terms of the basal elements of the algebra in the form

$$(26) \quad \omega_i = g_{i1}u_1 + g_{i2}u_2 + \cdots + g_{in}u_n, \qquad i = 1, \cdots, n.$$

The matrix of these coefficients (g_{ij}) is said to correspond to the given ideal. MacDuffee has then determined when two matrices correspond to different bases of the same ideal and when a matrix corresponds to an ideal. Greatest common divisor computations on the ideals can then be done elegantly in terms of computations of the greatest common left divisors of the corresponding matrices. Furthermore, the question of the equivalence of two ideals (in the sense that ideals are equivalent when they differ by factors which are principal ideals, cf. Sec. 4), which was discussed above in connection with hermitian forms, can be treated in terms of matrices. Thus the calculation of the number of classes of equivalent ideals becomes tangible.

9. CANONICAL FORMS FOR MATRICES

A matrix $A = (a_{ij})$ can always be considered as a linear transformation $y_i = \Sigma\, a_{ij} x_j$ $(i = 1, \cdots, n)$ which carries a vector $(x_1, \cdots, x_n)$ with n components into another vector $(y_1, \cdots, y_n)$. A change of the coordinate system to which these vectors are referred changes the matrix of the transformation to a new matrix.

$$(27) \qquad B = TAT^{-1} \qquad (T \text{ a nonsingular matrix}).$$

Such a B is called *similar* to A. Elementary divisors are ordinarily used to reduce A to a canonical form under such similarity transformations. Ingraham has considered this problem in the more general case when the matrix A is one whose elements are taken not in a field but in a division algebra. By using systematically the properties of the space which A transforms, he has been able to carry through the study of similarity in this case [14, 15]. Because the elements of the matrix are taken from an algebra without a commutative law, the polynomials in a matrix, which are important for the theory, must be redefined in a suitable manner. More generally, the equation (27) can be written in the form $BT = TA$, and this equation can be studied even when T is singular to determine the maximal possible rank for a matrix T satisfying the equation. Analogous methods work for other matrix equations [13].

When the elements of a matrix A are complex numbers, the matrix A is called *hermitian* if $A^* = A$, *unitary* if $AA^* = I$, where $A^* = (\bar{a}_{ji})$ is the conjugate transpose of the matrix A. The reductions of such matrices to canonical form by suitable similarity transformations are important classical problems. These problems can now be treated, as in Williamson [35], as a special type of a general reduction of certain normal matrices. A matrix is called *normal* if $AA^* = A^*A$. Both unitary and hermitian matrices have this property. It can be shown that a matrix A is normal in this sense if and only if A can be expressed as a polynomial $f(A^*)$ in its conjugate transpose matrix A^*. This leads to a more general definition: A matrix B is *normal* relative to a nonsingular hermitian matrix H if $BH = Hf(B^*)$ for some polynomial f. This includes the previous case with $H = I$. The canonical forms for such relatively normal matrices have been successfully treated by Williamson, using similarity transformations like (27) subject to the natural side condition that the given hermitian matrix H be unchanged by T in the sense that $THT^* = H$.

10. LIE ALGEBRAS

In the study of the so-called *commutators* of a group of continuous transformations certain nonassociative algebras arise. These algebras differ from the linear associative algebras considered above essentially in the replacement of the associative law of multiplication by two other laws:†

$$(28) \quad [x, y] = -[y, x], \qquad [x[y, z]] + [y[z, x]] + [z[x, y]] = 0.$$

Here, in accord with usage, the product of two elements in a Lie algebra is denoted by $[x, y]$. Such a Lie algebra may readily be obtained from an associative algebra A by the simple device of defining the multiplication of the Lie algebra in terms of the given associative multiplication by the equation

$$[x, y] = xy - yx,$$

so that $[x, y]$ is the "commutator" of x and y. The fact that the so-defined commutator actually satisfies the conditions (28) can be readily verified. By using a suitable automorphism S of the given associative algebra A, it is possible to define still other Lie algebras and even to describe their automorphism groups. By systematic use of such construction Jacobson has reduced the problem of determining all "simple" Lie algebras over ordinary fields to questions in underlying associative algebras. These questions can be solved explicitly when the algebra is one over the field of real numbers, but here, as in Cartan's classical theory of Lie groups, certain troublesome exceptional algebras can arise.

---

† These laws are not unfamiliar. They are satisfied by the vector product of two vectors. For a complete definition of terms, see Jacobson [16, 17].

11. LOCAL CLASS FIELD THEORY

An extraordinary combination of the study of fields with valuations, algebraic extensions of fields, automorphism groups of fields and normal simple algebras over fields has arisen in the class field theory. This theory aims at an explicit description of the fields K which are abelian extensions of an algebraic number field k. An *abelian* extension of k is a normal extension of k (*cf.* footnote in Sec. 7) such that the group of all automorphisms (6) of K which leave k fixed is *abelian*. The class field theory describes these extensions in terms of automorphism groups by a device which represents the automorphism group in terms of an isomorphic group derived from the multiplicative group in the field k [4]. Furthermore, the character of these abelian extensions proves to be intimately connected to the variety and the properties of the normal simple algebras and cyclic algebras possible over k. For many purposes this study of fields and algebras over the rational number field k can be simplified by treating each prime number in k separately; one then considers the extensions not of k but of the p-adic field k_p which is complete with respect to the p-adic valuation (5) defined by this prime p. Schilling has shown in several papers [28, 29, 30] that most of the theorems of local class field theory can also be obtained over fields k complete with respect to more general valuations. The p-adic valuations (5) are *discrete* in the sense that the value $V(a)$ of every element a of the field is an integer, but the abelian extensions turn out to have much the same structure if one considers valuations in which $V(a)$ runs over all rational numbers or even includes some irrationalities.

12. WHAT IS ALGEBRA?

To summarize this survey we shall essay here a description of the general tendency of these investigations. Algebra concerns itself with the postulational description of certain systems of elements in which some or all of the four rational operations are possible: fields, linear algebras, Lie algebras, groups. The abstract or postulational development of these systems must then be supplemented by an investigation of their "structure." Under "structure" we include:

(a) the number and interrelations of the subsystems of a given system, either subsystems just like the whole system (lattice of subgroups), or subsystems with especially characteristic properties (sets of integers, maximal orders, ideals, subfields of an algebra, etc.);

(b) the group of automorphisms of a system, and connections between the subgroups of this group and the subsystems of the given system (Galois theory, class field theory);

(c) the construction of all systems of specific types out of simpler systems of the same or other types (the construction of cyclic algebras and matrix algebras, the reduction of a given surface to a birationally equivalent surface without singularities, construction of Lie algebras);

(d) alternatively, the description of given systems as subsystems of larger systems (complete fields, power series fields);

(e) criteria or invariants to determine when two explicitly but differently constructed systems are abstractly the same or *isomorphic* (the canonical generation of a cyclic algebra; the genus as an invariant defined by the differentials of a function field).

With this explanation we venture the characterization: *Algebra tends to the study of the explicit structure of postulationally defined systems closed with respect to one or more rational operations.*

This summary does not account well for the use of topological operations in algebra, of which the valuations form but one example. Furthermore, the reduction of matrices to canonical forms is only indirectly an instance of the criteria intended in (e). As with many hypergeneralizations, our statements fit the facts only when the facts are first slightly distorted!

BIBLIOGRAPHY

1. Albert, A. A., *Modern Higher Algebra*. Chicago: University of Chicago Press, 1937.

2. Albert, A. A., "Integral domains of rational generalized quaternion algebras," *Bulletin of the American Mathematical Society,* Vol. 40 (1934), pp. 164–176.

3. Albert, A. A., "On cyclic algebras," *Annals of Mathematics,* Vol. 39 (1938), pp. 669–682.

4. Artin, E., "Beweis des allgemeinen Reziprozitätsgesetzes," *Abhandlungen aus dem Mathematischen Seminar, Hamburg,* Vol. 5 (1927), pp. 353–363.

5. Baer, R., "Abelian groups without elements of finite order," *Duke Mathematical Journal,* Vol. 3 (1937), pp. 68–122.

6. Birkhoff, G., "On the combinations of subalgebras," *Proceedings of the Cambridge Philosophical Society,* Vol. 29 (1933), pp. 441–464.

7. Brauer, R., "Über die Konstruktion der Schiefkörper, die von endlichem Rang in bezug auf ein gegebenes Zentrum sind," *Journal für die Mathematik,* Vol. 168 (1932), pp. 44–64.

8. Deuring, M., "Algebren," *Ergebnisse der Mathematik und ihrer Grenzgebiete,* Vol. 4, Part 1 (1935).

9. Dickson, L. E., *Algebren und ihre Zahlentheorie.* Zürich, 1927.

10. Eichler, M., "Neuere Ergebnisse der Theorie der einfachen Algebren," *Jahresbericht der Deutschen Mathematiker-vereinigung,* Vol. 47 (1937), pp. 198–220.

11. Hasse, H., "Darstellbarkeit von Zahlen durch quadratische Formen in einem beliebigen algebraischen Zahlkörper," *Journal für die Mathematik,* Vol. 153 (1924), p. 113.

12. Hull, R., "Maximal orders in rational cyclic algebras of odd prime degree," *Transactions of the American Mathematical Society,* Vol. 38 (1935), pp. 515–530.

13. Ingraham, M. H., "On certain equations in matrices whose elements belong to a division algebra," *Bulletin of the American Mathematical Society,* Vol. 44 (1938), pp. 117–124.

14. Ingraham, M. H., and M. C. Wolf, "Relative linear sets and similarity of matrices whose elements belong to a division algebra," *Transactions of the American Mathematical Society,* Vol. 42 (1937), pp. 16–31.

15. Jacobson, N., "Pseudo-linear transformations," *Annals of Mathematics,* Vol. 38 (1937), pp. 484–507.

16. Jacobson, N., "Rational methods on the theory of Lie algebras," *Annals of Mathematics,* Vol. 36 (1935), pp. 875–881.

17. Jacobson, N., "Abstract derivation and Lie algebras," *Transactions of the American Mathematical Society*, Vol. 42 (1937), pp. 206–224.

18. Latimer, C. G., "On ideals in generalized algebras and Hermitian forms," *Transactions of the American Mathematical Society*, Vol. 38 (1935), pp. 436–446.

19. Latimer, C. G., "On the fundamental number of a rational generalized quaternion algebra," *Duke Mathematical Journal*, Vol. 1 (1935), pp. 433–435.

20. Latimer, C. G., "On the class number of a quaternion algebra with a negative fundamental number," *Transactions of the American Mathematical Society*, Vol. 40 (1936), pp. 318–323.

21. Lefschetz, S., *Lectures in algebraic geometry* (mimeographed). Princeton University, 1937.

22. MacDuffee, C. C., "Ideals in linear algebras," *Bulletin of the American Mathematical Society*, Vol. 37 (1931), pp. 841–853.

23. MacDuffee, C. C., "Matrices with elements in a principal ideal ring," *Bulletin of the American Mathematical Society*, Vol. 39 (1933), pp. 564–584.

24. MacLane, S., "The uniqueness of the power series representation of certain fields with valuations," *Annals of Mathematics*, Vol. 39 (1938), pp. 370–382.

25. Ore, O., "On the foundations of abstract algebra," *Annals of Mathematics*, Vol. 37 (1936), pp. 265–292.

26. Ostrowski, A., "Algebraische Funktionen von Dirichletschen Reihen," *Mathematische Zeitschrift*, Vol. 37 (1933), pp. 98–133.

27. Perlis, S., "Maximal orders in rational cyclic algebras of composite degree," *Bulletin of the American Mathematical Society*, Vol. 44 (1938), p. 356.

28. Schilling, O. F. G., "The structure of local class field theory," *American Journal of Mathematics*, Vol. 60 (1938), pp. 75–100.

29. Schilling, O. F. G., "Class fields of infinite degree over p-adic number fields," *Annals of Mathematics*, Vol. 38 (1937), pp. 469–476.

30. Schilling, O. F. G., "A generalization of local class field theory," *American Journal of Mathematics*, Vol. 60 (1938), pp. 667–705.

31. Schmidt, F. K., "Zur arithmetischen Theorie der algebraischen Funktionen, I," *Mathematische Annalen*, Vol. 41 (1936), pp. 415–438.

32. Walker, R. J., "Reduction of the singularities of an algebraic surface," *Annals of Mathematics*, Vol. 36 (1935), pp. 336–365.

33. Wedderburn, J. H. M., "Lectures on matrices," *Colloquium Publications of the American Mathematical Society*, Vol. 17 (1934).

34. Witt, E., "Theorie der quadratischen Formen in beliebigen Körpern," *Journal für die Mathematik*, Vol. 176 (1937), pp. 31–44.

35. Williamson, J., "Matrices normal with respect to a Hermitian matrix," *American Journal of Mathematics*, Vol. 60 (1938), pp. 355–373.

36. Zariski, O., "Polynomial ideals defined by infinitely near base points," *American Journal of Mathematics*, Vol. 60 (1938), pp. 151–204.

This bibliography, prepared in 1938, might today be supplemented by many other articles and books; we list here only a few of the more accessible texts.

37. Albert, A. A., *Structure of Algebras*. New York: American Mathematical Society Colloquium Publications, Vol. 24, 1939.

38. Artin, E., and J. Tate, *Class Field Theory* (mimeographed notes). Cambridge: Harvard University, 1960.

39. Birkhoff, G., *Lattice Theory*. New York: American Mathematical Society Colloquium Publications, Vol. 25, rev. ed., 1948.

40. Birkhoff, G., and S. MacLane, *A Survey of Modern Algebra*, rev. ed. New York: The Macmillan Company, 1953.

41. Jacobson, N., *Lie Algebras*. New York: Interscience Tracts in Pure and Applied Mathematics, No. 10, 1962.

42. Jenner, W. E., *Rudiments of Algebraic Geometry*. New York: Oxford University Press, 1963.

43. Lang, S., *Introduction to Algebraic Geometry*. New York: Interscience Tracts in Pure and Applied Mathematics, No. 5, 1958.

44. O'Meara, O. T., *Introduction to Quadratic Forms*. Heidelberg: Springer Verlag and New York: Academic Press, Grundlehren der mathematishen Wissenschaft, Vol. 117, 1963.

SOME ADDITIONAL ADVANCES IN ALGEBRA

Saunders MacLane

The preceding article, "Some Recent Advances in Algebra," took the occasion of a conference on algebra held at the University of Chicago in 1938 to try to summarize the state of development of algebra at that time. In the intervening 24 years many problems, then current, have been solved or considerably advanced, while new problems and new directions of research have developed. The result is a second revolution in the character of algebra, fully as important as the dramatic growth of abstract algebra in the decade 1925–1935. Here we shall illustrate this revolution by a few samples, chosen from among those familiar to the author. The section numbers continue those of the previous article.

13. FINITE GROUPS

Perhaps the simplest concept of abstract algebra is that of a group: a set G of elements $g, h, \cdots$, each pair of which has a "product" gh in G. The axioms require that this product is associative, that there is in G an identity element 1 with $g1 = g = 1g$

for every g, and that for each g there is an "inverse" element g^{-1} with $gg^{-1} = 1$. The simplicity of these axioms is deceptive, for they actually impose a great deal of structure on the set G, notably when G is a finite set. In this case the number of elements in the set G is called the *order* of the group G.

The examination of all possible finite groups was a lively topic of research in the decade 1900–1910. It turned out to be a tough topic, since it rapidly appeared that there was no easy way of listing all possible finite groups, and the gradual development of more sophisticated concepts led to problems of great technical difficulty. The last few years have seen a dramatic breakthrough due to the emergence of powerful new techniques.

A typical question is that of determining whether a given group G is or is not finite. The group is "given," say, by a finite number of elements which generate the group and which satisfy certain specified relations. Burnside's famous conjecture (about 1900) is a case in point. Let n and k be given positive integers, suppose that G is generated by k elements $a_1, \cdots, a_k$ and that the nth power of every element of G is 1. This means that G consists of all "words" which can be written as iterated products of the generators and their inverses, say $a_1 a_2 a_3^{-1}$, $a_2^2 a_1 a_4^{-1} a_5$, and that the nth power of any such word is equal to 1. This requirement implies that certain formally distinct words are equal. Question: is G necessarily finite? One form of Burnside's conjecture guesses "yes."

With only one generator ($k = 1$), G consists of the n distinct elements $1, a_1, a_1^2, \cdots, a_1^{n-1}$ (a cyclic group) and is surely finite. With $k \geq 2$ generators and exponent $n = 2$, "yes" is also correct. Indeed, if g and h are any two elements, then $g^2 = 1$, $h^2 = 1$, and moreover $1 = (gh)^2 = ghgh$. Multiply the last equation on the left by g and on the right by h to get $gh = g^2 hgh^2 = hg$; this states that any two elements g and h in G must commute. Any element of G can now be written in terms of the generators in their given order as $a_1^{e_1} a_2^{e_2} \cdots a_k^{e_k}$ with exponents e_i either 0 or 1. Using all possible choices of these exponents, there are at most 2^k different elements in G.

Much more sophisticated arguments succeeded in proving Burnside's group finite for $n = 3$, for $n = 4$, and, in a recent paper by Marshall Hall [17], for $n = 6$. The prospect of continued slow progress on this problem was drastically altered by Novikov's announcement [28] that the Burnside group (with at least two generators) is infinite for any exponent $n \geq 72$. His proof, not yet published in full, uses an elaborate combinatorial analysis of possible cancellations between different words, a solution of a special case of a "word problem" due to Tartakovskii [35], and a result from "symbolic dynamics." The latter, found long ago by M. Morse, is an infinite sequence of two symbols 0 and 1 in which no block of symbols is repeated three times in succession. The reader might enjoy the ingenious but elementary construction of this sequence [24].

But do not imagine that the mysteries of Burnside's conjecture are all settled. There is another version (the "restricted" problem): consider those Burnside groups which are finite; is there a biggest one? For this problem a positive solution in the case of a prime exponent $n = p$ has recently been found by Kostrikin (see Higman [19]), using methods of Lie algebras.

14. SIMPLE GROUPS

For a fixed element g in a group G we may form for each element h of G a conjugate element $c_g(h) = ghg^{-1}$; if we regard c_g as a function mapping G onto G, this function is an automorphism of G, in the sense that $c_g(h_1h_2) = c_g(h_1)c_g(h_2)$. Recall that a subgroup S of G is a subset of G such that s_1 and s_2 in S imply $s_1s_2^{-1}$ in S; any such S is itself a group. Among the subgroups of G it is important to consider the *normal* subgroups N: those subgroups N of G such that every conjugate $c_g(n)$ of an element n of N also lies in N. Normal subgroups arise from homomorphisms. If G and G' are groups, a *homomorphism* $\gamma: G \longrightarrow G'$ is a function on G to G' which preserves the products $(\gamma(g_1g_2) = (\gamma g_1)(\gamma g_2)$ for all g_1, g_2 in G). It follows that $\gamma 1 = 1$. The kernel K of γ is defined to be the set of all those elements k in G with $\gamma(k) = 1$; it is always a normal subgroup of G. Conversely, to each normal subgroup N of G there is a group G/N and a homomorphism $G \longrightarrow G/N$ with image G/N

and with exactly N as its kernel. These properties describe the "factor group" G/N uniquely (up to isomorphism); they indicate that each normal subgroup $N \lhd G$ yields a decomposition of G into two "smaller" groups, N and G/N. A group is called *simple* if it has no normal subgroups except the obvious ones, G itself and 1. The finite simple groups are "building stones" for more complicated groups. Hence the problem of analyzing the possible finite simple groups.

A cyclic group of prime order is simple, so is the alternating group of all even permutations of n letters when $n \geq 5$. Many other simple groups can be derived from geometric considerations, say by suitable constructions on the group of all nonsingular matrices with entries in a finite field. These geometric considerations can best be viewed in terms of Lie algebras and a study of algebraic groups by the techniques of algebraic geometry, as formulated recently by Chevalley [12]. It is a fascinating and unsolved question to determine whether all simple groups (except for the alternating groups and a few other known exceptions) have such a "geometric" origin.

It is instructive to examine a list of the known simple groups (Artin [1]). Long ago Burnside observed that every known finite simple group (except the cyclic ones) had order divisible by 12; he conjectured that this order was always divisible by 2 (not 12!). Much excitement attended the recent discovery of some new finite simple groups by Suzuki [34] and Ree [29, 30]. Ree found two families of examples by Chevalley's Lie algebra methods. The reader may enjoy consulting Suzuki's elementary description of his family of examples (which can also be had by geometric devices, using the so-called *simplectic* groups). The striking fact is that his simple groups have order *not* divisible by 3, showing that Burnside made an informed guess. Just recently Feit and Thompson have announced a proof [41] of his guess: *Any* finite simple group is necessarily either cyclic or of even order.

15. ARITHMETIC STRUCTURE OF GROUPS

The study of special classes of groups is suggested by the composition series. Call a normal subgroup N of G *maximal* if it is

properly contained in G and if there is no intermediate subgroup
M, $N < M < G$, also normal in G. In a given finite group G
choose any maximal normal subgroup N_1; within N_1 choose a
maximal normal subgroup N_2 (normal as a subgroup of N_1, but not
necessarily as a subgroup of G) and so on, to get a "composition
series" $G \triangleright N_1 \triangleright N_2 \triangleright \cdots \triangleright N_k$ which eventually ends with the
subgroup consisting of 1 alone. All the groups N_i which can be
so obtained are called *subnormal* groups of G. The Jordan-Hölder
theorem asserts that the corresponding sequence of factor groups
G/N_1, N_1/N_2, $\cdots$ is, except for order and isomorphism, independent of the successive choices of N_1, N_2, $\cdots$. Since each N_i is
chosen as large as possible, each of these factor groups is a simple
group. If all these factor groups are cyclic (each of order some
prime), G is called *solvable*. Thus the conjecture (end of Sec. 14)
on simple groups can be restated: Every finite group of odd order
is solvable.

Among the solvable groups are the *nilpotent* groups. First observe that from any two finite groups G and H, we can construct
a new group $G \times H$, the *cartesian product*, with elements the pairs
(g, h) of elements g in G and h in H, and with product taken termwise, as in $(g_1, h_1)(g_2, h_2) = (g_1 g_2, h_1 h_2)$. For example, the cartesian
product of two solvable groups can be easily seen to be solvable.
A *nilpotent* group can be defined to be a group of the form
$G = G_1 \times \cdots \times G_t$, where each factor G_i is a group whose order
is some power of a prime p_i (such a G_i is called a p_i-*group*). Here
the arithmetic structure of the prime numbers really enters. In any
text on group theory, the reader may find the easy proof that in
any p-group G there is an element $g_0 \neq 1$ which commutes with
every element of G. This has the consequence that any p-group is
solvable, and hence that any nilpotent group (as a cartesian
product of p-groups for various primes p) is solvable. On the other
hand, the symmetric group S_4, consisting of all permutations of
four given marks, is solvable, but not nilpotent; indeed, its solvability is the reason for the solvability of polynomial equations of
the fourth degree by radicals.

We have introduced these two classes of groups in order to
formulate two recent theorems which give considerable insight

into the structure of finite groups. A subgroup M of G is said to be *maximal* if there is no subgroup of G properly containing M. Some time ago Schmidt and Iwasawa proved that if *every* maximal subgroup of G is nilpotent, then G is solvable. Recently Thompson [36, 37] proved that if just *one* maximal subgroup M of G is nilpotent and has odd order, then G is solvable. Secondly, an automorphism θ of G is an isomorphism $\theta \colon G \longrightarrow G$; we have already observed that conjugation provides one example of such an automorphism. The order of the automorphism θ is the least integer m such that $\theta^m(g) = \theta\theta \cdots \theta(g) = g$ for every g. In answer to a long-standing problem of Frobenius, Thompson showed that if a finite group G has an automorphism θ of prime order which leaves only the identity element fixed, then G is nilpotent. The techniques used to prove these two results are too complex for summary here; suffice it to say that they appear to provide a penetrating approach to many of the basic questions of group theory.

16. LATTICES AND GROUPS

Lattice theory, as described in the preceding article, was one of the dominant new fields of research in the decade of the 30's. In subsequent developments it has had a less central position in algebraic research, but the reader may easily see the extent of advance by comparing the two editions of Birkhoff's definitive book [7]. Investigations of the structure of the lattice of subgroups of a group have continued; as a sample we mention the beautiful theorem of Wielandt [39] which states that the subnormal subgroups of a group G, as defined above, form a lattice. It is relatively easy to see that the intersection of any two subnormal subgroups of G is again a subnormal subgroup (the reader may wish to show this for himself, using the fact that the intersection of two normal subgroups of G is again a normal subgroup of G); the weight of the proof resides in showing that the join of two subnormal subgroups is again subnormal.

In the sequel we deal with *abelian* groups, where the product is commutative; in this case the "product" is written as a sum $g + h$, and the "identity element" as 0.

17. LOCAL RINGS

Recall that a ring R is a set of elements $a, b, c, \cdots$, closed under two binary operations, addition and multiplication; R is required to be an abelian group under addition, and the multiplication is required to be associative and distributive:

$$(1) \qquad a(bc) = (ab)c, \quad a(b + c) = ab + ac, \quad (b + c)a = ba + ca.$$

Moreover, we shall require that the ring R have a multiplicative *identity* element 1, such that always $a1 = a = 1a$. (Earlier algebra studied rings which did not necessarily possess such an identity, but most of the interesting rings *do* have an identity, and current studies usually assume its presence.) If R' is a second such ring, a homomorphism $\rho: R \longrightarrow R'$ is a function on R to R' such that

$$(2) \qquad \rho(ab) = (\rho a)(\rho b), \quad \rho(a + b) = \rho a + \rho b, \qquad \rho 1 = 1'.$$

The *kernel* of ρ is the set of elements k in R with $\rho(k) = 0$. In case every element of R' has the form $\rho(a)$ for some a in R, we say that ρ is *onto* R'.

A (two-sided) *ideal* L in a ring R is a subset of R which is an additive subgroup of R and such that $r \in R$ and $l \in L$ always implies rl and $lr \in L$; in other words, the ideal must be closed under addition and multiplication, left or right, by any element of the ring. One shows at once that the kernel K of any homomorphism $\rho: R \longrightarrow R'$ is an ideal in R. Conversely, given an ideal $L \neq R$ one may form a ring R/L and a homomorphism $\rho: R \longrightarrow R/L$ onto R/L which has exactly L as its kernel; this property characterizes the "quotient ring" R/L. The whole ring R and the set (0) consisting of the zero element 0 alone are ideals in R; any other ideal is said to be a *proper* ideal in R.

Now let R be a commutative ring ($ab = ba$ always). To each element a of R we may construct the set $(a) = \{ra\}$ of all multiples ra of a by any element r of R; this set is an ideal, indeed, it is the smallest ideal of R containing a, and is called the *principal* ideal generated by a. Similarly, if $a_1, \cdots, a_m$ are m given elements of R, the set of all sums $r_1a_1 + \cdots + r_ma_m$ with coefficients r_i in R is an ideal of R, denoted by $(a_1, \cdots, a_m)$; it is the smallest ideal of R containing $a_1, \cdots, a_m$. The commutative ring R is said to be *noetherian* if every ideal has this form. It is equivalent to require that R have no infinite ascending sequence of ideals $L_1 < L_2 < L_3 < \cdots$, each properly containing the previous one.

A unit u of R is an element of R which has an inverse v in R (with $vu = 1$). The principal ideal (u) generated by u is then the whole ring R, for $r = r1 = (rv)u$. Conversely, any proper ideal L in R can contain no unit u of R.

Our previous article noted the utility in algebraic geometry of a particular ring, the ring R of all formal power series

$$A = a_0 + a_1t + a_2t^2 + \cdots$$

in a symbol t with coefficients a_i in some fixed field. By calculating the formal inverse of the series A, it is easy to see that A is a unit in the ring R if and only if the first coefficient a_0 is nonzero. On the other hand, the set M of all *nonunits* of the ring R is an ideal in R, for this set consists of all those formal series A with first coefficient $a_0 = 0$, so is clearly closed under addition and under multiplication by any series in R. We have already noted that any proper ideal L of R contains only nonunits of R, so must be contained in this ideal M, which is thus *the* maximal (proper) ideal of the power series ring R. (The corresponding quotient ring R/M is just the field of coefficients.)

Similarly, the ring of all formal power series

$$a_0 + a_1t + b_1s + a_2t^2 + b_2st + c_2t^2 + \cdots$$

in two (or more) symbols s, t has a maximal ideal M consisting of all nonunits. Again, for each prime p the field R_p of p-adic numbers (Sec. 1) contains a ring J_p of p-adic integers (those p-adic numbers x with valuation $V_px \geq 0$), and in this ring the nonunits form an ideal. These examples are typical rings for algebraic number and algebraic function theory, and illustrate the notion of a *local ring*: a commutative noetherian ring R in which *all* the nonunits form an ideal M. This ideal is then necessarily the maximal proper ideal of R, containing all other proper ideals. Many of the recent developments of commutative algebras and ideal theory center around the properties of such local rings, as first introduced by Krull [20]. We shall give some examples of such results in Sec. 22 below and also refer the reader to the books by Northcott [27], Zariski-Samuel [40], and Nagata [44].

Another example of local rings arises from the consideration of prime ideals. An ideal $P \neq R$ in the commutative ring R is said to be *prime* if $ab \in P$ implies that either a or b is in P. Given a prime ideal P, we may imitate the construction of fractions, forming a new ring R_P whose elements are those formal quotients a/b with denominator b *not* in P, and with the usual equality $(a/b = a'/b'$ if and only if $ba' = ab')$ and the usual sum and product of formal quotients. It follows that the units of R_P are those formal quotients a/b with neither a nor b in P. Therefore all the nonunits form an ideal M which is thus the maximal ideal in this ring R_P. Thus R_P is a local ring; it is known as a *ring of quotients* of R. In particular, if R is an integral domain, the set (0) consisting of zero alone is a prime ideal and $R_{(0)}$ is just the field of quotients of the integral domain R, in the usual sense. If R is the ordinary ring of integers, and p a prime number, the principal ideal (p) of all multiples of p is a prime ideal and $R_{(p)}$ is the ring of those (ordinary) rational numbers with denominators prime to p.

18. MODULES AND TENSOR PRODUCTS

In linear algebra and matrix theory the notion of a vector space over a field is a basic one; recently the more general notion of a module over a ring has come into prominence. In euclidean n-space a vector a with components $x_1, \cdots , x_n$ can be described simply as the n-tuple $a = (x_1, \cdots , x_n)$ of these components; each such vector can be multiplied by any real number r to give a new vector $ra = (rx_1, \cdots , rx_n)$ and two vectors can be added termwise as

$$(x_1, \cdots , x_n) + (y_1, \cdots , y_n) = (x_1 + y_1, \cdots , x_n + y_n);$$

all the vectors form an abelian group under this addition. Since the same geometric vector can equally well be described by its components with respect to a different basis, it is more apposite to describe the space of all n-dimensional vectors by the formal properties of these operations of addition and multiplication by scalars. In this description replace the scalars (field of real numbers) by an arbitrary commutative ring R; the result is the notion of an R-module.

Specifically, an R-*module* is an abelian group A together with a rule which defines for each $r \in R$ and $a \in A$ a "multiple" $ra \in A$ which satisfies

(3) $r(a + b) = ra + rb,$ $(rs)a = r(sa),$ $1a = a.$

For example, the ring R itself may be regarded as an R-module, any ideal K in R is an R-module, since K is closed under addition and multiplication by elements of R, and this multiplication satisfies (3). Similarly, each quotient ring R/K may be regarded as an R-module. If R is a field F, then an F-module is just a vector space over F, but since a field has no proper ideals the F-modules (vector spaces) have a particularly simple structure. If A and B are two R-modules, their direct sum $A \oplus B$ is the set of all ordered pairs (a, b) with $a \in A$ and $b \in B$, with addition and multiplication by R defined by

(4) $(a_1, b_1) + (a_2, b_2) = (a_1 + a_2, b_1 + b_2),$ $r(a, b) = (ra, rb).$

There are iterated direct sums $A \oplus B \oplus C$; in particular, the n-fold iterated direct sum $R + \cdots + R$ of the R-module R is the free R-module on n generators $(0, \cdots, 1, \cdots, 0)$. When R is a field, this is just the n-dimensional vector space over that field.

If A and B are R-modules, a *homomorphism* (or linear transformation) $\alpha \colon A \longrightarrow B$ is a function on A to B which preserves the module operations in the sense that always

(5) $\alpha(a_1 + a_2) = \alpha a_1 + \alpha a_2,$ $\alpha(ra) = r(\alpha a).$

These imply $\alpha 0 = 0$. The *kernel* of the homomorphism α is the set of all a in A with image zero $(\alpha a = 0)$; it is a "submodule" of A. The *image* of α is the set of all αa for $a \in A$; it is a submodule of B. If $\beta \colon B \longrightarrow C$ is another homomorphism, the composite $\beta\alpha$ (first α, then β) is the function on A to C with $\beta\alpha(a) = \beta(\alpha(a)) \in C$; it is a homomorphism $\beta\alpha\colon A \longrightarrow C$. A particularly important case is that in which the kernel of the second homomorphism β is exactly the image of α (then $\beta\alpha$ is zero, and "just barely" zero). In this case, the pair of homomorphisms $A \longrightarrow B \longrightarrow C$ is said to be *exact* at B. For the zero module 0, consisting of 0 alone, there are always homomorphisms $0 \longrightarrow A$ and $B \longrightarrow 0$. To say that $A \xrightarrow{\alpha} B \longrightarrow 0$ is exact is thus to say that every element of B is an image αa of some $a \in A$, or that α is an epimorphism (*onto* B). Also $0 \longrightarrow A \xrightarrow{\alpha} B$ is exact if the kernel of α consists of 0 alone, so in this case α is a monomorphism (one-one into B).

There are two basic constructions, Hom and $\otimes$, of new modules from given ones. For A and B fixed R-module, two homomorphisms $\alpha_1, \alpha_2\colon A \longrightarrow B$ have a sum $\alpha_1 + \alpha_2$ defined by $(\alpha_1 + \alpha_2)a = \alpha_1 a + \alpha_2 a$ for each a in A; this sum is again an R-module homomorphism $\alpha_1 + \alpha_2\colon A \longrightarrow B$. Likewise the multiple $r\alpha$ given by $(r\alpha)a = r(\alpha a)$ is an R-module homomorphism, for $r\alpha$ so defined carries sums into sums and scalar multiples into such; indeed, because R is commutative,

$$(r\alpha)(r'a) = r[\alpha(r'a)] = (rr')(\alpha a) = r'[r(\alpha a)] = r'[(r\alpha)a].$$

The set $\text{Hom}_R (A, B)$ of all R-module homomorphisms $\alpha\colon A \longrightarrow B$ is thus closed under operations of addition and multiplication by elements of R, and is itself an R-module under these operations.

A "tensor product" $A \otimes_R B$ of two R-modules may also be constructed. It is the abelian group with generators $a \otimes b$, one for each pair of elements $a \in A$, $b \in B$, subject to the relations

(6) $$a \otimes (b_1 + b_2) = a \otimes b_1 + a \otimes b_2,$$

$$(a_1 + a_2) \otimes b = a_1 \otimes b + a_2 \otimes b,$$

(7) $$a \otimes rb = ra \otimes b.$$

Thus $0 = a \otimes 0 = 0 \otimes b$, $-(a \otimes b) = (-a) \otimes b$, and an element of $A \otimes_R B$ is a finite sum $\Sigma\, a_i \otimes b_i$ of generators; two such sums are equal if the first can be transformed into the second by a finite sequence of relations of the form (6), (7). To each such element $\Sigma\, a_i \otimes b_i$ and each $r \in R$ we may define a multiple

$$r(\Sigma \, a_i \otimes b_i) = \Sigma \, ra_i \otimes b_i = \Sigma \, a_i \otimes rb_i;$$

with this definition $A \otimes_R B$ becomes itself an R-module.

A function $h(a, b)$ on two R-modules A and B to a third R-module C is said to be *bilinear* if, for each fixed a_0 in A, $h(a_0, b)$ is a homomorphism $B \longrightarrow C$ and for each fixed b_0 in B, $h(a, b_0)$ is a homomorphism $A \longrightarrow C$. Thus the definition of $A \otimes_R B$ above has exactly the form to make $a \otimes b$ a bilinear function on A, B to $A \otimes_R B$. Moreover—and this is the basic property— for *any* bilinear function h there is a unique homomorphism $\gamma \colon A \otimes_R B \longrightarrow C$ such that $h(a, b) = \gamma(a \otimes b)$. In this sense, $a \otimes b$ is a "universal" bilinear function.

If A and B are vector spaces over a field F, their tensor product $A \otimes_F B$ turns out to be just the set of all tensors with two (contravariant) indices, in the usual sense of the word "tensor." Mixed covariant and contravariant tensors with more indices can be described by similar constructions (Chevalley [12]); in particular, the tensor product is associative, since there is a "natural" isomorphism

$$(A \otimes_R B) \otimes_R C \cong A \otimes_R (B \otimes_R C).$$

The systematic use of Hom_R and $\otimes_R$ exploits the behavior of these functions under homomorphisms of modules. Thus two module homomorphisms $\alpha \colon A \longrightarrow A'$ and $\beta \colon B \longrightarrow B'$ yield a module homomorphism

(8) $\alpha \otimes \beta \colon A \otimes_R B \longrightarrow A' \otimes_R B'$

defined by the rule $(\alpha \otimes \beta)(a \otimes b) = \alpha a \otimes \beta b$. If we take $\alpha = 1_A$ to be the identity homomorphism of A to itself, $1 \otimes \beta = \beta_*$ is the homomorphism induced by β on the tensor product. Similarly for Hom_R there are induced homomorphisms

(9) $\beta_* \colon \mathrm{Hom}_R (A, B) \longrightarrow \mathrm{Hom}_R (A, B'),$

                        $\alpha^* \colon \mathrm{Hom}_R (A', B) \longrightarrow \mathrm{Hom}_R (A, B)$

defined for each $f \in \mathrm{Hom}_R (A, B)$ as

$$\beta_* f = \beta f \colon A \longrightarrow B' \quad \text{and} \quad \alpha^* f = f\alpha \colon A \longrightarrow B.$$

Note, in particular, that the direction of α^* (from A' to A) is the reverse of the direction of α. The effect of these induced homomorphisms upon exactness is a starting point of homological algebra (Cartan-Eilenberg [11], MacLane [43], Northcott [26]).

19. CATEGORIES

Homomorphisms may be defined for each type of algebraic system; in the last twenty years it has become clear that the formal properties of the class of all homomorphisms repay independent study. This leads to the notion of "category" and "functor."

A *category* consists of a class of "objects" and a class of "morphisms" which may be combined under a suitable composition of morphisms. For example, if R is a fixed commutative ring, then the category $\mathfrak{M}_R$ of all R-modules has as its "objects" all R-modules $A, B, C, \cdots$: to each pair of objects there is a set $\text{Hom}_R (A, B)$ of "morphisms," consisting of all the R-module homomorphisms $\alpha\colon A \longrightarrow B$. The composite $\beta\alpha$ of two morphisms is defined exactly when they fit, as in $\alpha\colon A \longrightarrow B$, $\beta\colon B \longrightarrow C$, and the composite is a morphism $\beta\alpha\colon A \longrightarrow C$. The axioms for a category demand only that this composite satisfy the associative law $\gamma(\beta\alpha) = (\gamma\beta)\alpha$ whenever the composites involved are defined, and that to each object there be an identity morphism $1_B\colon B \longrightarrow B$ with $1_B\alpha = \alpha$ and $\beta 1_B = \beta$. The constructions $\text{Hom}_R (A, B)$ and $A \otimes_R B$ are functions (of two variables) on this category to itself; when the appropriate properties of these functions with respect to composition of induced morphisms are considered, they become *functors*.

One may similarly construct the category of groups: objects, all groups; morphisms, all homomorphsims of groups. Again, the category of topological spaces has morphisms all continuous maps of one topological space onto another. The category $\mathfrak{M}_R$ of all R-modules has important special properties, arising from the fact that each set of morphisms $\text{Hom}_R (A, B)$ is actually an abelian group; moreover, each morphism has a kernel and an image (and dually, a cokernel and a coimage) with appropriate properties. Such categories—known as abelian categories—may be regarded as generalized rings (ringoids)—since they are sets of morphisms *some* pairs of which can be added, and *some* pairs multiplied—with the formal laws of a ring holding true whenever they make sense.

Like the notion of a lattice, the concept of a category belongs to universal algebra. It was first introduced in 1945 [13]; abelian categories first appeared in 1950 [21] and were developed in [9] and [15]. For details see [43].

20. HOMOLOGICAL ALGEBRA

An R-module P is said to be *projective* if it has the following property. For every homomorphism $\alpha\colon P \longrightarrow C$ into any other R-module C and for every epimorphism $\beta\colon B \longrightarrow C$, as in the diagram

(10)

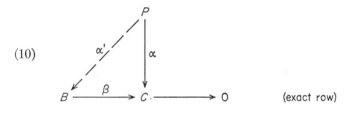

(exact row)

there exists a homomorphism $\alpha'\colon P \longrightarrow B$ such that the composite $\beta\alpha'$ is α (i.e., such that the triangular diagram becomes "commutative"). In other words, P is projective if every homomorphism α with P as domain can be "lifted" through each epimorphism B. For example, the ring R itself is a projective R-module, for given $\alpha\colon R \longrightarrow C$ and β an epimorphism there is a $b \in B$ with $\beta b = \alpha(1)$, and the requisite α' may be defined as $\alpha'(r) = rb$, so that

$$\beta\alpha'(r) = \beta(rb) = r(\beta b) = r\alpha(1) = \alpha(r).$$

Similarly any direct sum $P = R \oplus \cdots \oplus R$ is projective, and more generally, any free R-module on an infinite number of free generators is projective.

In case R is a field, every R-module ($=$ vector space) is free and hence automatically projective. But for a general ring R most modules are not projective and projective modules are not necessarily free. The importance of projective modules was emphasized in the pioneering book by Cartan-Eilenberg [11] on homological algebra. They have turned out to be the proper tool for the study of linear algebra for modules which are not vector spaces.

These projective modules are used to describe the "homological dimension" of an R-module A. If A is generated by n elements $a_1, \cdots, a_n$, we may form a free module F on n generators $x_1, \cdots, x_n$ and define an epimorphism $\epsilon: F \longrightarrow A$ with $\epsilon(x_i) = a_i$. The kernel K of F is again an R-module; its injection into F yields a sequence of homomorphisms $0 \longrightarrow K \longrightarrow F \longrightarrow A \longrightarrow 0$ which is exact (at K, F, and A). The kernel K may be regarded as the module of "relations" on the generators a_i of A; it may again be written as a quotient $F_1 \longrightarrow K \longrightarrow 0$ of a new free module F_1; this yields a longer exact sequence $0 \longrightarrow K_1 \longrightarrow F_1 \longrightarrow F \longrightarrow A \longrightarrow 0$. In continuing the process, it is not necessary to require that A be finitely generated, and it is appropriate to replace the free modules by projective modules. Thus each module A has a projective resolution; that is, there is an exact sequence, starting with A and continuing with projective modules P in the form

$$\cdots \longrightarrow P_n \longrightarrow \cdots \longrightarrow P_2 \longrightarrow P_1 \longrightarrow P_0 \longrightarrow A \longrightarrow 0.$$

Though this resolution is not unique, any two such can be "compared" via the basic property (10) of a projective module.

The module A has homological *dimension* at most n, if there is such a resolution with $P_{n+1} = 0$. For example, if the ring R is a field, every R-module A is a vector space, hence is free, hence has a projective resolution $0 \longrightarrow A \longrightarrow A \longrightarrow 0$, so has dimension 0. If R is the ring of integers, an R-module is just an abelian group. Every subgroup of a free abelian group is itself free, so here every R-module has a projective resolution $0 \longrightarrow K \longrightarrow F \longrightarrow A \longrightarrow 0$, so the homological dimension of A is at most 1. The further investigation of such homological dimensions, notably in the case when R is a ring of polynomials (the Hilbert syzygy theorem), has been extensively developed in recent years.

An exact sequence $0 \longrightarrow A \longrightarrow B \longrightarrow C \longrightarrow 0$ of R-modules does not remain exact when we take its tensor product with another module D. This observation leads to the construction of a whole sequence of new functors $\operatorname{Tor}_n^R (C, D)$, $n = 0, 1, \cdots$ with $\operatorname{Tor}_0^R (C, D) = C \otimes_R D$. Similarly, the functor $\operatorname{Hom}_R (A, B)$ gives rise to a sequence of functors $\operatorname{Ext}_R^n (A, B)$. The explicit definition of these functors depends on a projective resolution of the module A or C and the formation of certain homology groups, after the manner of algebraic topology (see MacLane [22] [4] or Godement [14] for details). In fact, these constructions first arose in algebraic topology, where Tor_1 is needed to describe the homology of the cartesian product of two spaces, while Ext^1 occurs when the integral homology groups of a space are given and we wish to calculate for the space its cohomology with an arbitrarily given coefficient group.

21. HOPF ALGEBRAS

In 1939 an *algebra* meant a *finite*-dimensional vector space over a field, equipped with an associative and bilinear product (Sec. 6). Various applications in topology and analysis have forced a generalization. Today an algebra Λ is a module over a commutative ring R, still equipped with a "product." The product is a function which assigns to each pair of elements λ, $\mu \in \Lambda$ a unique element $\lambda\mu$ in Λ; this product is associative, that is, $(\lambda\mu)\nu = \lambda(\mu\nu)$, and bilinear as a function of λ and μ (this, of course, includes the distributive laws $\lambda(\mu + \nu) = \lambda\mu + \lambda\nu$). Now recall the basic property of the tensor product $\Lambda \otimes_R \Lambda$. To say that the function $\lambda\mu$ is bilinear amounts to saying that there is a unique homomorphism $\pi\colon \Lambda \otimes_R \Lambda \longrightarrow \Lambda$ with $\pi(\lambda \otimes \mu) = \lambda\mu$; thus a bilinear product can be described as a homomorphism π. The associativity of the product now amounts to the statement that the following diagram

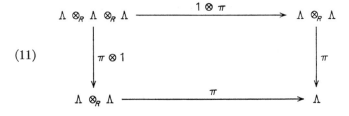

(11)

is commutative. Here, as in (8), $1 \otimes \pi$ is the homomorphism

$$\lambda \otimes \mu \otimes \nu \longrightarrow \lambda \otimes \pi(\mu \otimes \nu).$$

A similar diagram will formulate the condition that the algebra has an identity element. (Cf. Guggenheim [42].)

The prime advantage of this diagrammatic description of an algebra as a module with a suitable homomorphism $\pi\colon \Lambda \otimes \Lambda \longrightarrow \Lambda$ is that it can be dualized. The process of dualization amounts to "reversing all the arrows." Hence we define: A *coalgebra* over the commutative ring R is an R-module U together with a homomorphism $\psi\colon U \longrightarrow U \otimes_R U$ of R-modules such that the diagram

(12)

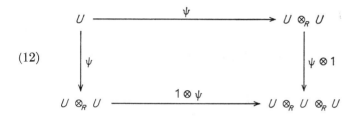

is commutative. A similar condition will state that the coalgebra U has a dual identity element. We call ψ the *coproduct* or the *diagonal* map of U. For example, the ring R itself is a coalgebra, with $\psi(r) = r \otimes 1 = 1 \otimes r$. A more instructive example takes U to be the usual ring $R[x]$ of all polynomials $f = a_0 + a_1 x + \cdots + a_n x^n$ in an indeterminate x with coefficients a_i in the given ground ring R. Since the coproduct ψ is a homomorphism,

$$\psi(\Sigma\, a_i x^i) = \Sigma\, a_i \psi(x^i),$$

so it suffices to define the coproduct $\psi(x_n)$ for each power x_n of the indeterminate, say by the formula

$$(13) \quad \psi(x^n) = x^n \otimes 1 + nx^{n-1} \otimes x + \cdots + (i, j)x^i \otimes x^j \\ + \cdots + 1 \otimes x^n, \qquad (i + j = n),$$

where $(i, j) = (n!)/((i!)(j!))$ is the usual binomial coefficient; one may then check the commutativity condition (12) on each generator x^n. For $n = 1$, this formula reads $\psi(x) = x \otimes 1 + 1 \otimes x$;

in any coalgebra U, those elements u for which the coproduct is simply $\psi(u) = u \otimes 1 + 1 \otimes u$ are said to be *primitive elements* of U.

Finally, a Hopf algebra is an R-module H which is both an algebra with respect to a product map $\pi: H \otimes H \longrightarrow H$ and a coalgebra with respect to a coproduct $\psi: H \longrightarrow H \otimes H$, related to each other by the requirement that the diagram

(14)

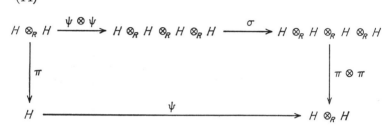

be commutative. Here σ is the homomorphism which interchanges the middle two factors according to the formula

$$\sigma(h_1 \otimes h_2 \otimes h_3 \otimes h_4) = h_1 \otimes h_3 \otimes h_2 \otimes h_4.$$

This somewhat mysterious diagram can be made more intelligible if one remarks that the tensor product $H \otimes_R H$ of any algebra with itself is also an algebra with product map defined by $(\pi \otimes \pi)\sigma$; then (14) states in effect that the coproduct $\psi: H \longrightarrow H \otimes_R H$ is a homomorphism of the algebra H to the algebra $H \otimes_R H$. There is a dual interpretation of this diagram (14) via tensor products of coalgebras. As an example note that the ring $R[x]$ of polynomials is an algebra under the usual multiplication of polynomials; it is also a coalgebra under the coproduct ψ defined in (14), and it may be verified that this product and coproduct together satisfy the condition (14). Indeed, the coproduct ψ in this case is determined by (14) and the requirement that x be primitive.

Such algebras first occurred in topological investigations; H. Hopf observed that the (singular) cochains of a topological group constitute a Hopf algebra in the above sense with the coproduct induced by the multiplication in the topological group and the product given by the standard cup product of cochains. Again, the singular chains of any topological space form a coalgebra, with coproduct the dual of the usual cup product of cochains. These examples have indicated the relevance of an algebraic study of the structure of coalgebras and Hopf algebras, as initiated in the investigations of A. Borel, Halpern [18], and Milnor-Moore [23]. In this study the primitive elements of a coalgebra play a role dual to that of the "indecomposable" elements of an algebra Λ (the indecomposable elements of Λ may be described as the elements of the factor module $\Lambda/[\pi(\Lambda \otimes \Lambda)]$).

22. UNIQUE FACTORIZATION IN LOCAL RINGS

The new discipline of homological algebra has served to solve several outstanding problems in the theory of local rings. Among the local rings, as described in Sec. 17, there is a class of well-behaved local rings known as the *regular* local rings, described by a suitable property of their prime ideals. These are the local rings which occur for algebraic varieties, essentially as the ring of algebraic functions regular at a given point of the variety. It has proved possible to characterize the regular local rings among all local rings by the requirement that a certain homological dimension be finite (Serre [32], Auslander-Buchsbaum [2, 3]). Using this characterization it is possible to prove that every ring of quotients of a regular local ring is again regular, a result previously conjectured but known only in special cases of geometric interest.

The unique factorization property holds in many familiar commutative rings: every element of the ring can be written as a product $p_1 p_2 \cdots p_k$ of indecomposable or "prime" elements, and this factorization is unique except for the order of factors and the insertion and removal of factors which are units. Unique factorization is known to hold in the ring of integers, in the ring of polynomials in one or more variables with coefficients in a field, in the ring of p-adic integers, and in the ring of all formal power series in one or more variables, again with coefficients in a field. These last two cases suggested the long-standing conjecture: Unique factorization holds in any regular local ring. This conjecture has recently been established; it was reduced to the case of "dimension 3" by Nagata [25], and then was proved in this difficult case, using the techniques of homological algebra, by Auslander-Buchsbaum [4].

23. ALGEBRAIC GEOMETRY

The systematic investigation of the basic concepts of algebraic geometry, and especially of the notion of intersection multiplicity, as carried out in A. Weil's treatise [38], pointed up the strongly algebraic character of this subject. In recent years this has been carried much further, making still heavier use of the properties of rings, and with emphasis on categories and functors. A new basic notion, that of a schema, has been introduced, to make more effective the passage from the characteristic 0 to the characteristic p case, and thus to relate algebraic geometry to the appropriate number-theoretical questions about diophantine equations in several variables. These developments, though by no means finished, seem to presage an exciting revolution in algebraic geometry. For Riemann surfaces (algebraic functions of one variable) a classical result was the Riemann-Roch theorem which determines the number of linearly independent meromorphic functions on a Riemann surface which have (at most) a specified finite set of poles. This was extended to algebraic varieties by Hirzebruch and others; more recently the techniques of Grothendieck have given a much more general such Riemann-Roch theorem (see the theorem as formulated in Borel-Serre [8]). Grothendieck and Dieudonné are currently engaged in the preparation of an extensive treatise on this line of development [16]. This can be regarded as an algebraization of another field of mathematics.

24. THE NATURE OF ALGEBRA

The previous article concluded with an attempt to characterize algebra as the study of "structure" of systems defined by suitable postulates on rational operations. Today this characterization seems naive and somewhat limited. Portions of abstract algebra can, indeed, be construed as investigations of such structure theorems. But as the present article indicates, the development of the subject is much more varied. Older questions, such as those about finite group theory, return to the center of interest with the developments of new ideas and techniques; they cannot always be simply categorized as "structure theory." New types of algebraic systems arise from the applications of algebra in geometry, topology, and analysis. Thus the study of Hopf algebras and of coalgebras was suggested by the investigation of topological groups; many applications forced modules into a central position, tensor products arose from differential geometry, categories and homological algebra from topology. The types of algebraic systems to be analyzed are suggested and imposed by various other mathematical uses, and the development of algebra can be understood only within the fabric of all mathematics.

BIBLIOGRAPHY

1. Artin, E., "The orders of the classical simple groups," *Communications on Pure and Applied Mathematics* (NYU), Vol. 8 (1955), pp. 455–472.

2. Auslander, M., and D. A. Buchsbaum, "Homological dimension in noetherian rings," *Proceedings of the National Academy of Sciences of the United States of America*, Vol. 42 (1956), pp. 36–38.

3. Auslander, M., and D. A. Buchsbaum, "Homological dimension in local rings," *Transactions of the American Mathematical Society*, Vol. 85 (1957), pp. 390–405.

4. Auslander, M., and D. A. Buchsbaum, "Unique factorization in regular local rings," *Proceedings of the National Academy of Sciences of the United States of America*, Vol. 45 (1959), pp. 733–734.

5. Auslander, M., and O. Goldman, "Maximal orders," *Transactions of the American Mathematical Society*, Vol. 97 (1960), pp. 1–25.

6. Auslander, M., and O. Goldman, "The Brauer group of a commutative ring," *Transactions of the American Mathematical Society*, Vol. 97 (1960), pp. 367–410.

7. Birkhoff, G., *Lattice Theory*. Providence: American Mathematical Society Colloquium Publication No. 25, 1938, rev. ed., 1948.

8. Borel, A., and J. P. Serre, Le Théorème de Riemann-Roch, *Bulletin de le société mathématique de France*, Vol. 86 (1958), pp. 97–136.

9. Buchsbaum, D. A., "Exact categories and duality," *Transactions of the American Mathematical Society*, Vol. 80 (1955), pp. 1–34.

10. Burnside, W., *Theory of Groups of Finite Order*, 2nd ed. Cambridge University Press, Cambridge, 1911, reprinted Dover Publications, New York, 1955.

11. Cartan, H., and S. Eilenberg, *Homological Algebra*. Princeton: Princeton University Press, 1956.

12. Chevalley, C., "Sur certains groupes simples," *Tôhoku Mathematical Journal*, Vol. 7 (1955), pp. 14–66.

13. Eilenberg, S., and S. MacLane, "General theory of natural transformations," *Transactions of the American Mathematical Society*, Vol. 50 (1945), pp. 231–294.

14. Godement, R. *Théorie des Faisceaux*, Actualités scientifique et industrielles, No. 1252. Paris: Hermann, 1958.

15. Grothendieck, A., "Sur quelques points d'algebre homologique," *Tôhoku Mathematical Journal*, Vol. 9 (1957), pp. 119–221.

16. Grothendieck, A., and J. Dieudonné, *Éléments de Géométrie Algébrique*, I. *Le Langage des Schemas*, Publications Mathématiques No. 4, pp. 1–228. Paris: Institut des Hautes Études Scientifiques, 1960.

17. Hall, M. Jr., "Solution of the Burnside problem for exponent 6," *Proceedings of the National Academy of Sciences of the United States of America*, Vol. 43 (1957), pp. 751–753.

18. Halpern, E., *Twisted Polynomial Hyperalgebras*, Memoirs of the American Mathematical Society, No. 29, 61 pp. Providence: American Mathematical Society, 1958.

19. Higman, G. A., "Lie ring methods in the theory of finite nilpotent groups," *Proceedings*, International Mathematical Congress, Edinburgh, 1958. New York: Cambridge University Press, 1960.

20. Krull, W., "Dimensionstheorie in Stellenringen," *Journal für die reine und angewandte Mathematik*, Vol. 179 (1938), pp. 204–226.

21. MacLane, S., "Duality for groups," *Bulletin of the American Mathematical Society*, Vol. 56 (1950), pp. 485–516.

22. MacLane, S., Review of *Homological Algebra, Bulletin of the American Mathematical Society,* Vol. 62 (1956), pp. 615–624.

23. Milnor, J. W., and J. C. Moore, "On the structure of Hopf algebras," to appear, *Annals of Mathematics.*

24. Morse, M., and G. A. Hedlund, "Unending chess, symbolic dynamics and a problem in semigroups, *Duke Mathematical Journal,* Vol. 11 (1944), pp. 1–7.

25. Nagata, M., "A general theory of algebraic geometry over Dedekind rings, II," *American Journal of Mathematics,* Vol. 80 (1958), pp. 382–420.

26. Northcott, D., *Homological Algebra.* New York: Cambridge University Press, 1961.

27. Northcott, D., *Ideal Theory,* Cambridge Tracts in Mathematics and Mathematical Physics No. 42. New York: Cambridge University Press, 1953.

28. Novikov, "On periodic groups," *Doklady Akademii Nauk S.S.S.R.,* Vol. 127 (1959), pp. 749–752 [reviewed in *Mathematical Reviews* No. 5680, Vol. 21 (October, 1960)].

29. Ree, R., "A family of simple groups associated with the simple Lie algebra of type (F_4)," *Bulletin of the American Mathematical Society,* Vol. 67 (1961), pp. 115–116.

30. Ree, R., "A family of simple groups associated with the simple Lie algebra of type (G_2)," *Bulletin of the American Mathematical Society,* Vol. 66 (1960), pp. 508–510.

31. Samuel, P., "On unique factorization domains," *Illinois Journal of Mathematics,* Vol. 5 (1961), pp. 1–17.

32. Serre, J. P., "Sur la dimension homologique des anneaus et des modules noetheriens," *Proceedings,* International Symposium on Algebraic Number Theory, Tokyo and Nikko, 1955, pp. 176–189. Tokyo: Science Council of Japan, 1956.

33. Suzuki, M., "On finite groups with cyclic Sylow subgroups for all odd primes," *American Journal of Mathematics,* Vol. 77 (1955), pp. 657–691.

34. Suzuki, M., "A new type of simple groups of finite order," *Proceedings of the National Academy of Sciences of the United States of America,* Vol. 46 (1960), pp. 868–870.

35. Tartakovskii, V. A., "The sieve method in group theory; Application of the sieve method to the solution of the word problem for certain types of groups; Solution of the word problem for groups with k-reduced basis for $k > 6$, *American Mathematical Society Translation*, No. 60 (1952).

36. Thompson, J. G., "Finite groups with fixed-point-free automorphisms of prime order," *Proceedings of the National Academy of Sciences of the United States of America*, Vol. 45 (1959), pp. 578–581.

37. Thompson, J. G., "Normal p-complements for finite groups," *Mathematische Zeitschrift*, Vol. 72 (1960), pp. 332–354.

38. Weil, A., *Foundations of Algebraic Geometry*, American Mathematical Society Colloquium Publications, No. 29. Providence: American Mathematical Society, 1946.

39. Wielandt, H., "Eine Verallgemeinerung der invarianten Untergruppen," *Mathematische Zeitschrift*, Vol. 49 (1939), pp. 209–244.

40. Zariski, O., and P. Samuel, *Commutative Algebra*, Vols. I and II. Princeton: D. van Nostrand Co., 1958 and 1960.

41. Feit, Walter, and J. G. Thompson, "A solvability criterion for finite groups and some consequences," *Proceedings of the National Academy of Sciences of the United States of America*, Vol. 48 (1962), pp. 968–970.

42. Guggenheim, V. K. A. M., "On extensions of algebras, co-algebras, and Hopf algebras, Part I," *American Journal of Mathematics*, Vol. 84 (1962), pp. 349–382.

43. MacLane, S., *Homology*. Heidelberg and Berlin: Springer Verlag, Grundlehren der mathematishen Wissenschaft, Vol. 114, 1963.

44. Nagata, M., *Local Rings*. New York: John Wiley and Sons, Interscience Tracts in Pure and Applied Mathematics, 1962.

WHAT IS A LOOP?†

R. H. Bruck

1. INTRODUCTION

The main intent of this paper is to exhibit loops in relation to elementary topics which will not require too much mathematical background from the reader. We bring out some of the connections with Steiner triple systems (Sec. 5), latin squares (Sec. 6), geometric nets (Sec. 7), geometric axioms (Sec. 8), and a new type of experimental design (Sec. 10). At various points we have suggested a few exercises, of varying degrees of interest or difficulty, to a total of about 30.

The reader who wants to go further into these topics, or into the theory of loops proper, will find some help in Sec. 2 (which contains some remarks on the use of the bibliography) and in Sec. 11 (which discusses references supplementary to those in the main body of the paper).

† During the preparation of this paper the author was supported by a grant from the National Science Foundation.

In discussing loops it is natural to begin with groupoids and semigroups (Sec. 3) and quasigroups (Sec. 4). Then we embark on the topics mentioned in the first paragraph. The only topic of pure loop theory is the nonassociative integers (Sec. 9). The only places where we ask for much mathematical knowledge are toward the end of Sec. 10 and in the latter half of the Appendix, where we make use of abelian groups and finite fields.

2. REMARKS ON REFERENCES

The author's book *A Survey of Binary Systems* (the first reference in the bibliography at the end of the paper) will be denoted by [S] and will be used for two distinct purposes which we now explain.

A number of topics, which we wish neither to ignore entirely nor to treat in detail in the present article, will be found in [S]. Notations such as [SI.4], [SII Theorem 3.4], or [S p. 45] refer to Chap. 1, Sec. 4, to Chap. II, Theorem 3.4, or to page 45, respectively, of [S].

The bibliography in [S] is almost exhaustive up until 1957 or a little later. For this reason, the bibliography at the end of the present paper is largely limited to quite recent literature. Thus, if n is a positive integer, $[n]$ denotes the item numbered n in the bibliography at the end of this paper, whereas $[Sn]$ denotes the item numbered n in the bibliography of [S].

One further remark on bibliography should prove helpful to the reader. *Mathematical Reviews* (now in its twentieth year, and to be found in any good university library) contains brief reviews of nearly all research papers and advanced textbooks on mathematics published since 1938, usually with a delay of about a year. Before going to much expense to obtain a copy of a paper (authors often furnish free copies; journals can be borrowed or bought; microfilms or photostats of specific articles can frequently be purchased), the reader should consult the review in *Mathematical Reviews*. With this in mind, wherever possible, each listing in the bibliography (at the end of this paper or in [S] is followed by a reference to *Mathematical Reviews*. For the first 19 volumes of *Mathematical*

Reviews the reference takes the form MR x, y (meaning that the review is on page y of volume x). Beginning with Vol. 20, the form is MR $x,$ No. z (denoting review numbered z of volume x).

3. GROUPOIDS

A *groupoid* (sometimes called a *multiplicative system*) is a pair (G, o) consisting of a nonempty set G and a *binary operation* o subject only to the axiom

(I) *If a, b are in G, there exists one and only one c in G such that $a o b = c$.*

Groupoids are exteremely common in mathematics. For the most part, they are not very interesting in their own right, but only with reference to topics in which they are almost unnoticed. We shall give three familiar examples, stating first the set G and then the form of a o b:

(1) *The positive real numbers; $a o b = a^b$,*
(2) *The nonnegative real numbers; $a o b = |a - b|$, where $|x|$ denotes the absolute or numerical value of x;*
(3) *The nonnegative real numbers rounded off to one decimal place, with a fixed rule for rounding (always to the larger or always to the smaller choice) in case of ambiguity; a o b is the result of rounding ab.*

A groupoid (G, o) is called a *semigroup* if it satisfies the *associative law*:

(A) $(a o b) o c = a o (b o c)$ *for all a, b, c in G.*

Although there is a very large literature of semigroups (e.g., $[Sx]$ for $153 \leq x \leq 324$ and $360 \leq x \leq 424$) the discussion of semigroups would carry us far from the topic of loops. We merely wish to show that each of the examples (1), (2), (3) fails to be a semigroup:

In case (1), $(2 o 2) o 3 = 4 o 3 = 64$, whereas $2 o (2 o 3) = 2 o 8 = 256$. This explains the need for careful use of parentheses in connection with exponentiation.

In case (2), (1 o 2) o 3 = 1 o 3 = 2, whereas 1 o (2 o 3) = 1 o 1 = 0.

In case (3), (2.1 o 3.3) o 5.7 = 6.9 o 5.7 = 39.3, whereas 2.1 o (3.3 o 5.7) = 2.1 o 18.8 = 39.5. This is a well-known phenemenon in connection with computing machines (where rounding, of course, is usually to ten or more decimal places).

These examples are intended to suggest to the reader that he or she has been dealing with groupoids for years and has been getting along quite nicely without the associative law.

Exercises. Make a list of various groupoids that you have encountered naturally in your mathematical studies and decide which of the groupoids are semigroups. (Don't forget the operations of addition, subtraction, multiplication, division, and averaging. Also consider some familiar functions of two variables.)

Literature. See [SI.1] and [Sx] for $32 \leq x \leq 53$ and $x = 346, 347$.

4. QUASIGROUPS, LOOPS, AND GROUPS

A *quasigroup* is a groupoid (G, o) which satisfies the axioms

(II) *If a, b are in G, there is one and only one x in G such that $a \circ x = b$.*

(III) *If a, b are in G, there is one and only one y in G such that $y \circ a = b$.*

Sometimes the axioms (I), (II), (III) for a quasigroup (G, o) are combined into one as follows: If any two of x, y, z are given as elements of G, the equation $x \circ y = z$ uniquely determines the third as an element of G. Quasigroups can also be studied as systems which are groupoids with respect to three (interrelated) operations; see [SI.2].

The requirement, in (II), (III), that x, y be unique, cannot be omitted. For example, if (G, o) is the example (2) of Sec. 3, the equation $a \circ x = b$ has at least one solution x for each choice of a, b in G; however, the equation 5 o $x = 2$ has the solutions $x = 3$

and $x = 7$. Example (2) could be described as a "division system" but not as a quasigroup.

A *loop* is a quasigroup (G, o) with an identity element; that is, a quasigroup satisfying:

(IV) *There exists an element e in G such that a* o *e* $= a =$ *e* o *a for every a in G.*

The identity element, e, is easily seen to be unique when it exists.

Axioms for a *group* can be given in various ways. One set of axioms is (I), (II), (III), and (A); and these imply (IV). Thus the terms "group," "associative quasigroup," and "associative loop" are synonymous. For further discussion of group axioms see [SII.3], Hall [2], or almost any book on group theory.

The *order* of a groupoid (for example, of a quasigroup, loop, or group) is the (finite or infinite cardinal) number of its elements.

In what follows we shall usually consider the operation to be multiplication; this is convenient since a o b can then be written more simply as ab. And, whenever special circumstances do not prevent us, we shall denote the identity element of a loop by 1.

If one hopes to go very deeply into the theory of loops, it is necessary to have a firm grasp of the theory of groups. In this paper, by arrangement of topics, we try to postpone the need for group theory until as late as possible.

5. STEINER TRIPLE SYSTEMS. TOTAL SYMMETRY

A *Steiner triple system* G^* of order n (where $n \geq 3$ is a positive integer) is a system consisting of a set G^* of order n whose n elements have been arranged in three-element subsets, called the *triples* of the system, subject to the following axiom:

(S) *If a, b are distinct elements of G^*, there is one and only one element c of G^* such that the elements a, b, c are distinct and form a triple of the system.*

If G^* is a Steiner triple system of order n and if $n - 1 = 2k$, $nk = 3t$, it is easy to see that k and t are positive integers. Indeed, every element of G^* is contained in exactly k of the triples; and the total number of triples is t. Clearly 3 is either a divisor of k or a divisor of n, so that n has one of the forms $6m + 1$, $6m + 3$ where m is an integer. That is, $n \equiv 1$ or 3 mod 6. Conversely (as Reiss [3] showed in 1859), if $n \geq 3$ and if $n \equiv 1$ or 3 mod 6, there exists at least one Steiner triple system of order n.

Our purpose here is to show that Steiner triple systems are co-extensive with a certain class of quasigroups (which are not loops) and also with a class of loops.

A quasigroup G (written multiplicatively) is called *totally symmetric* provided it satisfies the following axiom:

(TS) *If $ab = c$ and if a', b', c', are a, b, c in any order, then $a'b' = c'$.*

A quasigroup G is called *idempotent* if (where a^2 denotes aa)

(S) $a^2 = a$ *for all a in G.*

Now suppose that G^* is a Steiner triple system of order n. We may turn G^* into an idempotent totally symmetric quasigroup of order n by the following definitions:

(i) *if a, b are distinct elements of G^*, $ab = c$ where a, b, c is the triple of the system containing a, b;*
(ii) $a^2 = a$ *for all a in G^*.*

Conversely, every idempotent totally symmetric quasigroup of order $n \geq 3$ gives rise to a Steiner triple system of order n; we merely use (i) as a definition of the triples.

Next let us note that if G is a totally symmetric loop with identity element 1, then, since $1a = a$ for every a in G, we also have $a^2 = 1$ for every a in G. Totally symmetric loops can also be characterized among loops by the *commutative law*

(C) $ab = ba$ *for all a, b in G,*

together with the requirement that $a(ab) = b$ for all a, b in G.

Again let us suppose that G^* is a Steiner triple system of order n. Let $G = 1 \cup G^*$ be the set of $n + 1$ elements obtained by adjoining a new element 1 to G^*. We make G into a totally symmetric loop of order $n + 1$ by using (i) as before but replacing (ii) by the two rules which follow:

(ii') $1a = a1 = a$ *for all a in* G^*;
(ii'') $a^2 = 1^2 = 1$ *for all a in* G^*.

Conversely, every totally symmetric loop of order $n + 1$ (where n is at least 3) gives rise to a Steiner triple system of order n.

Notice that we can also go directly from an idempotent totally symmetric quasigroup of order n to a totally symmetric loop of order $n + 1$ and conversely. (Compare [S67], where the connection with Steiner triple systems was overlooked.)

Before proceeding we shall recall some concepts which are basic in much of mathematics and certainly in all of algebra. Let G, G' be nonempty sets (not necessarily distinct). By a *one-to-one mapping of G upon G'* we mean a "function" θ with the following properties:

(i) *if a is in G, there is one and only one a' in G' such that* $a\theta = a'$;
(ii) *if a' is in G', there is one and only one a in G such that* $a\theta = a'$.

Two one-to-one mappings, θ, ϕ, of G upon G' are *equal*, $\theta = \phi$, if and only if $a\theta = a\phi$ for every a in G. If θ is a one-to-one mapping of G upon G' and if ϕ is a one-to-one mapping of G' upon a nonempty set G'', the *product*, $\theta\phi$, is that one-to-one mapping of G upon G'' such that $a(\theta\phi) = (a\theta)\phi$ for all a in G. A *permutation* of a nonempty set G is a one-to-one mapping of G upon itself; the permutations of G form a multiplicative group.

Next let G, G' be (multiplicative) groupoids. An *isomorphism*, θ, of G upon G' is a one-to-one mapping of G upon G' such that $(ab)\theta = (a\theta)(b\theta)$ for all a, b in G. The groupoids G, G' are *isomorphic* if one (and hence either) possesses an isomorphism upon the other. (Note that *isomorphism* is the concept we are usually trying to convey when we tell a beginning student that two algebraic systems are "essentially the same.") An *automorphism* of a groupoid G is an isomorphism of G upon itself; the automorphisms of G form a multiplicative group.

Since Steiner triple systems are coextensive with (finite) idempotent totally symmetric quasigroups of order at least 3, it is obvious what we mean by isomorphic Steiner triple systems or by the automorphism group of a Steiner triple system. In any case, direct definitions could be given.

The literature of Steiner triple systems is very extensive. The main reference is Netto [4]; for a briefer account in English, see Carmichael [5]. Netto shows that (if isomorphic systems be counted as equal) there is just one Steiner triple system of each of the orders 3, 7, 9, but there are at least two nonisomorphic Steiner triple systems of every other order n (subject to the restrictions mentioned above). Carmichael constructs systems of various orders. Steiner triple systems have recently been attacked by high-speed computing machines (see Hall and Swift [S51]); the number of nonisomorphic systems of order 15 turns out to be 80.

From given Steiner triple systems we can obtain many more by taking direct products. We recall that the *direct product, $G \times H$,* of two multiplicative groupoids G, H, is the set of all ordered pairs (g, h), g in G, h in H, under the multiplication $(g, h)(g', h') = (gg', hh')$. The direct product of two quasigroups is a quasigroup; of two loops is a loop; of two groups is a group; of two idempotent (or totally symmetric) quasigroups is an idempotent (or totally symmetric) quasigroup. Now suppose we are given two Steiner triple systems of orders m, n, respectively. By taking direct products of the corresponding idempotent totally symmetric quasigroups of orders m, n, we get an idempotent totally symmetric quasigroup of order mn and hence a Steiner triple system of order mn. By taking direct products of the corresponding totally symmetric loops of orders $m + 1, n + 1$, we get a totally symmetric loop of order $(m + 1)(n + 1)$ and hence a Steiner triple system of order $mn + m + n$.

We should add the following to the preceding paragraph. There is (to within an isomorphism) only one quasigroup, E, of order 1, namely the group with one (identity) element e, satisfying $e^2 = e$. Thus E is both idempotent and totally symmetric. Similarly, there is only one quasigroup, T, of order 2, namely the group with elements 1, e, where 1 is the identity element and $e^2 = 1$. And T is a totally symmetric loop. The idempotent totally symmetric quasigroup E of order 1 and the totally symmetric loop T of order 2 do not correspond to a Steiner triple system (since we refuse to admit the degenerate "triple system" with one element). However, $T \times T$ corresponds to the unique Steiner triple system of order 3. Moreover, if G is any totally symmetric loop of order

$n + 1$, $n \geq 3$, then $G \times T$ is a totally symmetric loop of order $2n + 2$, corresponding to a Steiner triple system of order $2n + 1$.

The processes described in the last two paragraphs allow us to construct an infinite class of Steiner triple systems beginning with that of order 3. The set, S, of the orders of the systems thus obtained, may be defined inductively as follows:

(i) *3 is in S;*
(ii) *if n is in S, so is $2n + 1$;*
(iii) *if m, n are in S, so is mn;*
(iv) *if m, n are in S, so is $mn + m + n$.*

The first few integers in S, arranged in ascending order, are: 3, 7, 9, 15, 19, 21, 27, 31, 39, 43, 45, 49, 55. We notice that infinitely many possible orders are omitted, the first few being 13, 25, 33, 37, 51. More generally, if $p = 12k + 1$, $q = 6m - 1$, and $r = q + 12n$ are primes, then p, q^2 and qr are orders of Steiner triple systems but are not in S.

In order to fill the gaps in the list of orders we need some fairly sophisticated constructions which are relegated to an Appendix.

Exercise. Determine the idempotent totally symmetric quasigroups of orders 3, 7, 9 and the totally symmetric loops of orders 4, 8, 10. Show that the totally symmetric loops of orders 4 and 8 are groups but that that of order 10 is not a group.

6. CAYLEY TABLES. LATIN SQUARES

Suppose that G is a multiplicative groupoid of finite order n, and let $a_1, a_2, \cdots, a_n$ be the n elements of G arranged in any convenient order. We construct a *Cayley table* of G, consisting of n^2 cells, arranged in n (horizontal) rows and n (vertical) columns, as follows: If $a_i a_j = a_p$, the cell lying in the ith row, jth column of the table is to contain a_p. For example, the groupoid with elements 1, 2 in which $1 \cdot 2 = 2$ and all other products are 1 has the following table corresponding to the order 1, 2:

$$\begin{array}{cc} 1 & 2 \\ 1 & 1 \end{array}$$

If we write this as a "double-entry" multiplication table by adjoining a headline and sideline, it takes the clearer form:

	1	2
1	1	2
2	1	1

Now let us consider axiom (II). G satisfies (II) if and only if, for each fixed a_i in G, the product $a_i x$ ranges over the n distinct elements of G as x does; or, equivalently, if and only if each row of the Cayley table contains each element of G exactly once. Similarly, G satisfies (III) if and only if each column of the Cayley table contains each element of G exactly once.

Here we should recall that a *latin square* of order n is a square array of n rows and columns formed from n distinct objects and having the property that each row and column of the array contains each of the n objects exactly once. Hence: *a necessary and sufficient condition that a groupoid G of finite order should be a quasigroup is that one (and hence every) Cayley table of G be a latin square.*

Given one Cayley table of a groupoid, how do we get all the others? Obviously, we get them by performing (in all possible ways) the same permutation on the rows, on the columns, and on the entries (the n objects in the cells). In particular, two latin squares of order n obtainable from each other by such a process (coupled, perhaps, with a replacement of the n objects by another n objects) should properly be called *isomorphic*.

There is a broader relation between latin squares, known as *isotopy*. Two latin squares are called *isotopic* if one can be obtained from the other by using the following three types of operation:

(i) permutation of the rows;
(ii) permutation of the columns;
(iii) permutation of the objects in the cells (or replacing the objects by another set of objects).

For an abstract definition of isotopy of groupoids, etc., see [SIII.1].

If G is a loop of order n, we may always arrange the elements $a_1, a_2, \cdots, a_n$ so that a_1 is the identity element. Then the first row and first column of the Cayley contain the elements of G in the given order $a_1, a_2, \cdots, a_n$. The corresponding latin square is said to be *standard*. Obviously every latin square is isotopic to at least one standard square (and sometimes to several standard squares).

For very small values of n, lists may be found of standard latin squares of order n having the property that no two are isotopic and every latin square of order n is isotopic to one in the list. For $n = 3, 4, 5, 6, 7$, the number of nonisotopic latin squares of order n is 1, 2, 2, 17, 147. (For $n \leq 6$, see Fischer and Yates [6]; for $n = 7$, see Norton [7], Sade [8].) The corresponding numbers for $n \geq 8$ are all unknown—except that they are large! For $n = 3, 4, 5$, the number of nonisomorphic standard latin squares of order n is 1, 2, 5; if we allowed nonstandard squares, these numbers would be much increased. Moreover, Hall [9] has shown that the number of distinct latin squares of order n on a given set of objects is not less than the product $n!(n - 1)! \cdots 2!1!$, where $k!$ (or k factorial) means the product of the integers from 1 to k.

These remarks make it clear that finite loops and quasigroups are like grains of sand on a beach. Some of them may be interesting as indeed, some of them are! However, a detailed cataloguing of the loops and quasigroups (or groups and semigroups) of a given order is a job for librarians rather than mathematicians.

Exercises

1. Use latin squares to determine all loops of order $n \leq 4$. Show that these loops are groups.

2. Show that there is (to within an isomorphism) one and only one loop G of order 5 such that $a^2 = 1$ for all a in G. Verify that G is neither commutative nor associative but satisfies the identities $(ab)a = b = a(ba)$ for all a, b in G.

3. Use latin squares to answer the exercise in Sec. 5.

7. GEOMETRIC NETS

Let n, k be cardinal numbers, $n \geq 1$, $k \geq 3$. By a *net of order n, degree k* we mean a system N of objects called *points and lines*, together with an incidence relation, subject to the following axioms:

(I) *The lines of N are partitioned into k nonempty disjoint classes.*

(II) *If L, L' are lines of N belonging to different classes, there is one and only one point of N which is incident with both L and L'.*

(III) *If P is a point of N, then P is incident with one and only one line of each of the k classes.*

(IV) *There exists a line L of N such that there are exactly n distinct points of N which are incident with L.*

Turning to familiar language, we say that a point P is on (or lies on, or is a point of) a line L, and that L passes through (or contains) P, provided P is incident with L. Phrases such as "lines intersect" or "lines are concurrent" are also to be interpreted in terms of the incidence relation. Note that (I) and (II) ensure the existence of lines and of points. (III) states that each point lies on exactly one line of each class; (II) states that two lines of distinct classes have a unique point of intersection; (III) implies that two distinct lines of the same class are "parallel."

If L_1, L_2 are lines of distinct classes, then, since $k \geq 3$, there exists at least one line class K which does not contain L_1 or L_2. To each point P_1 of L_1 there corresponds exactly one line L of K which passes through P_1, and L meets L_2 in a unique point P_2. From this we may deduce that the number of points on L_1, the number of lines in K, and the number of points on L_2 are the same. Now it is easy to see the significance of the order n: Every line (of whatever class) of N contains exactly n distinct points, and every line class contains exactly n distinct lines. Moreover, the total number of distinct points is n^2, and the total number of distinct lines is nk.

There exist nets of order $n = 1$ and arbitrary degree k. Such nets are quite uninteresting and will be described as "trivial."

Next let N be a net of order $n > 1$ and degree k. Let P be a point of N. Since P lies on just one line of a class and since each class has $n > 1$ lines, there exists a line not through P. Let L be any line not through P. Of the k lines through P, one is parallel to L and the remaining $k - 1$ meet L in $k - 1$ distinct points. Since L has exactly n distinct points, we have $k \leq n + 1$. If $k = n + 1$, then every point of L lies on a line with P; in this case, every two distinct points of N lie on one and only one common line.

Now we have seen that, for a net N of order n, degree k, either $n = 1$ (the trivial net) or $k \leq n + 1$.

A net of order $n > 1$ and degree $k = n + 1$ is called a *Euclidean* (or *affine*) *plane of order* n. For an expository account of some of the theory of euclidean planes, see Bruck [10]. More advanced references are Pickert [11], Hall [2].

The connection between nets, quasigroups, and loops may be given as follows: Let N be a net of order n, degree k. Let A, G be arbitrary label sets, of k and n elements respectively. Label the line classes of N by the elements of A, so that we may speak of "class a" for each a in A. For each a in A, label the a-lines (i. e., the lines of class a) by the elements of G. Then, for each a in A, x in G, let (a, x) denote the a-line whose label is x. We select, arbitrarily, two distinct elements of A, say e, f. Then, for each a in A, $a \neq e, f$, we define an operation (a) on G as follows:

$$x(a)y = z$$

if and only if the lines (e, x), (f, y), and (a, z) are concurrent. In this way we define a quasigroup $(G, (a))$ for each a in A, $a \neq e, f$. Note also that if we permute the labels of lines independently in the three line classes labeled e, f and a, we merely replace $(G, (a))$ by an isotopic quasigroup.

When n, k are finite, the $k - 2$ quasigroups defined by the above process give rise to $k - 2$ latin squares of order n which are said to be *mutually orthogonal*. What this means can be explained as follows: Suppose $k \geq 4$, and let e, f, a, b be distinct elements of A. If p, q are given elements of G, the lines (a, p), (b, q) meet in a unique point P. Through P there is a unique e-line (e, x) and a unique f-line (f, y). Thus $x(a)y = p$, $x(b)y = q$. In other words, the Cayley table for $(G, (a))$ has p in row x, column y, while the Cayley table for $(G, (b))$ has q in row x, column y. Thus the corresponding latin squares have the property that, for each ordered pair p, q of elements of G, there is one and only one cell position (here given by row x, column y) such that the cell for the first latin square contains p and that for the second latin square contains q. This is the "orthogonality" property. Conversely, a set of $k - 2$ mutually orthogonal latin squares of order n gives rise to a net of order n and degree k.

Now let us consider a 3-net N (here $k = 3$) of (finite or infinite) order n. We may label the line classes by the numbers 1, 2, 3, and speak of 1-lines, 2-lines, and 3-lines. (It must be emphasized that we shall be using the three line classes in a fixed, nonsymmetrical fashion; a relabeling of the line classes will often give rise to a different class of isotopic loops.) With G as before, the lines of N will be denoted by $(1, x)$, $(2, y)$, $(3, z)$, where x, y, z are arbitrary elements of G. We make G into a multiplicative quasigroup by the requirement that $(1, x)$, $(2, y)$ and $(3, xy)$ shall be concurrent. We want to show that, by a suitable assignment of labels to the lines, G will actually be a loop. We do this as follows: Let I be an arbitrarily chosen point of the net N. Let 1 be an arbitrarily chosen element of G (which will turn out to be our identity element) and use this to label the lines through I. These are then $(1, 1)$, $(2, 1)$, $(3, 1)$. Next assign labels (from G) to the remaining lines of class 3 in any manner. Finally (see Fig. 1), label the remaining

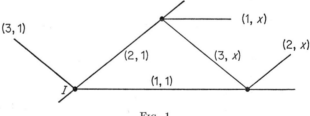

Fig. 1

lines of classes 1 and 2 so that $(1, x)$ meets $(3, x)$ on $(2, 1)$ and $(2, x)$ meets $(3, x)$ on $(1, 1)$. Now it follows from our definition of multiplication that $x1 = x$ (since $(1, x)$, $(2, 1)$, and $(3, x)$ are concurrent) and that $1x = x$ (since $(1, 1)$, $(2, x)$ and $(3, x)$ are concurrent) for every x in G.

We may define an isomorphic loop whose elements are points on the 1-line through I. This may be done without labeling of lines (though the line classes do need labels). However, in terms of the notation of the last paragraph, suppose that P, Q are points of $(1, 1)$, not necessarily distinct. Then (see Fig. 2) the unique 3-

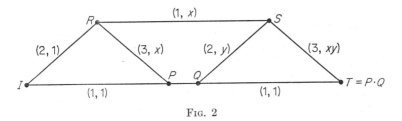

Fig. 2

line, $(3, x)$, through P meets $(2, 1)$ in a unique point R; the 1-line, $(1, x)$, through R, and the 2-line, $(2, y)$, through Q, meet in a point S; and the 3-line, $(3, xy)$, through S, meets $(1, 1)$ in a point T. We define the ordered product, $P \cdot Q$, of P and Q to be T. With this definition of our "point loop," I is the identity element.

In Figs. 1 and 2 we have drawn lines of the same class as though they were parallel lines in a plane. This is merely a convenience, even granted that the lines do not intersect in the net. Indeed (see [10]), both addition and multiplication in the ternary ring of a euclidean plane are defined in terms of 3-nets but one of the line classes for multiplication does not consist of parallel lines of the plane. (It might be appropriate to add here that the additive and multiplicative nets of a planar ternary ring, taken together, form a type of 4-net which satisfies axioms different from those considered in the present paper. For this subject, see Pickert [11].)

Given any loop (or quasigroup) G, we may construct a 3-net N (the net of G) as follows: The 1-lines, 2-lines, and 3-lines of N are the symbols $(1, x)$, $(2, x)$ and $(3, x)$ respectively, where x ranges over G. The points of N are the ordered couples $[x, y]$, where x, y range over G. A point $[x, y]$ is incident with the lines $(1, x)$, $(2, y)$ and $(3, xy)$, but with no other line of N. Note that, in Fig. 2, we

have $I = [1, 1], P = [1, x], Q = [1, y], R = [x, 1], S = [x, y],$
$T = [1, xy].$

The connection between 3-nets and loops is particularly useful when we wish to study some property of loops which is to hold not only for a given loop G but also for every loop isotopic to G. We shall give a well-known illustration in Sec. 8.

8. THE INVERSE PROPERTIES

First let G be a multiplicative group with identity element 1. If a, b are elements of G such that $ab = 1$, then, by the associative law, $(xa)b = x = a(bx)$ for every x in G. Here we intend to study loops with analogous properties.

A (multiplicative) loop G is said to have the *left inverse property* if to each element x in G there corresponds an element x^{-1} in G such that

$$(1) \qquad\qquad x^{-1}(xy) = y$$

for every y in G. (We observe, parenthetically, that quasigroups can have the left inverse property without being loops—for example, the idempotent totally symmetric quasigroups of Sec. 5.) From (1) with $y = 1$, we deduce that $x^{-1}x = 1$; in particular, this shows that x^{-1} is uniquely determined by x. From (1) with $y = x^{-1}$ we get $x^{-1}(xx^{-1}) = x^{-1}$, so that $xx^{-1} = 1$. Therefore

$$(2) \qquad\qquad xx^{-1} = 1 = x^{-1}x, \qquad (x^{-1})^{-1} = x.$$

A loop G is said to have the *right inverse property* if to each x in G there corresponds an element x^{-1} in G such that

$$(3) \qquad\qquad (yx)x^{-1} = y$$

for all y. Here again, (3) implies (2). A loop G is said to have the *inverse property* if the identities (1) and (3) hold simultaneously.

As pointed out in the first paragraph, every group has the inverse property. Again, every totally symmetric loop has the inverse property (Sec. 5), whence we see that loops with the inverse property need not be groups. In addition, loops exist with the left inverse property but not the right inverse property (or vice versa); and loops exist which fail even to satisfy (2).

There is an interesting connection between the inverse properties and certain geometric axioms for a 3-net. Let N be a 3-net and let L, M be lines of N belonging to the same line class. The following construction (see Fig. 3) allows us to determine another line,

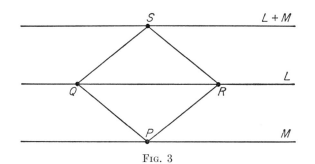

Fig. 3

$L + M$, which might be called the *reflection* of M in L: Select an arbitrary point P of M and let the other two lines of N which pass through P (i.e., those other than M) meet L in the points Q, R. Let the remaining line through Q and the remaining line through R meet in the point S. Then $L + M$ is the remaining line through S. (In particular, $L + M$ belongs to the same class as L and M.)

We note that if $L = M$, then $P = Q = R = S$ and $L + M = L = M$. In general, however, we should expect $L + M$ to depend on the choice of P. If we insist, on the contrary, that $L + M$ be independent of P, we get a geometric axiom (or "configuration theorem"). This axiom is generally split into three axioms, known as the *Moufang-Bol* axioms, according as the lines L, M are 1-lines, 2-lines, or 3-lines.

Let us suppose that the net N is coordinatized by a loop G, and let us consider the Moufang-Bol axiom for 1-lines. We assume (in Fig. 3) that $L = (1, x)$, $M = (1, y)$. Then $P = [y, p]$ where p is to be allowed to range over G. If PQ is the 2-line (and PR the 3-line) through P, then $PQ = (2, p)$, $PR = (3, yp)$. Since Q lies on $(1, x)$ and $(2, p)$, then $Q = [x, p]$. On the other hand, $R = [x, t]$, where t must satisfy $xt = yp$. Since QS is a 3-line, $QS = (3, xp)$; similarly, $RS = (2, t)$. Hence $S = [x + y, t]$ where

$(x + y)t = xp$. Thus, finally, $L + M = (1, x + y)$. To sum up, the Moufang-Bol axiom for 1-lines states that the equations

(4) $$xt = yp, \qquad (x + y)t = xp$$

determine a unique value for $x + y$ independently of p.

It is convenient, first, to consider the special case that the Moufang-Bol axiom for 1-lines is imposed only when L is the fixed line $(1, 1)$; that is, only for $x = 1$. When $x = 1$, (4) yields $t = yp$ and

(5) $$(1 + y)(yp) = p.$$

We note that (5) holds for all y, p, with $1 + y$ independent of p, if and only if G has the left inverse property. (Here, of course, $1 + y$ takes on the role of y^{-1} in the definition of the left inverse property.) Hence this restricted form of the Moufang-Bol axiom for 1-lines is precisely equivalent to the left inverse property for G.

In view of the geometric definition for multiplication (see Fig. 2), we see that the Moufang-Bol axiom for 1-lines is valid in a 3-net N if and only if every loop of the net has the left inverse property. Equivalently, one loop G of N has the left inverse property and every loop isotopic to G has the left inverse property.

Now we return to (4), assuming henceforth that G has the left inverse property. Solving for t from the first equation of (4), we get $t = x^{-1}(yp)$. Hence

(6) $$(x + y)[x^{-1}(yp)] = xp,$$

where $x + y$ is to be independent of p. If we set $p = y^{-1}(xz)$, and make two uses of the left inverse property, (6) becomes

(7) $$(x + y)z = x[y^{-1}(xz)],$$

where $x + y$ is to be independent of z. Setting $z = 1$ in (7), we get

(8) $$x + y = x(y^{-1}x).$$

Finally, by substituting from (8) in (7), and then replacing y by y^{-1}, we get

(9) $$[x(yx)]z = x[y(xz)]$$

for all x, y, z.

It is not difficult to show that a loop satisfying the identity (9) also satisfies the left inverse property (essentially, we merely note what happens in (9) if we choose y so that $yx = 1$). Then, as before, we may eliminate t from (4) to get (6). And, finally, by (9) and the left inverse property, we see easily that (6) holds for all x, y, p when $x + y$ is defined by (8). To sum up, we have proved the following theorem of Bol [S66]:

A necessary and sufficient condition that the net defined by a loop G should satisfy the Moufang-Bol axiom for 1-lines is that G satisfy the identity (9).

By a precisely similar analysis, we may show that the Moufang-Bol axiom for 2-lines is equivalent both to the identity

$$(10) \qquad z[(xy)x] = [(zx)y]x$$

and to the property that the loop G and every loop isotopic to G has the right inverse property.

The Moufang-Bol axiom for 3-lines cannot be expressed as an identity involving only the multiplicative operation in the loop G. However, as originally shown by Bol [S66], any two of the three Moufang-Bol axioms imply the third. A 3-net satisfying the three Moufang-Bol axioms is called a *Bol* net.

Now, for a moment, let G be any loop with the inverse property. Setting $xy = z$, we get $x^{-1}z = y$ by (1), $yz^{-1} = x^{-1}$ by (3), and $y^{-1}x^{-1} = z^{-1}$ by (1) again. Thus

$$(11) \qquad (xy)^{-1} = y^{-1}x^{-1}$$

for all x, y in G. Next let G be any loop satisfying the identity (11); then it is obvious that G satisfies (9) if and only if G satisfies (10).

Again, let G be a loop with the inverse property which satisfies (9). From (1) with $z = x^{-1}$,

$$[x(yx)]x^{-1} = xy,$$

and thence, by the right inverse property,

$$(12) \qquad x(yx) = (xy)x$$

for all x, g in G. Note that, when (12) holds, the product xyx is unambiguous.

As we have noted, the identities (9), (10), which correspond to the Moufang-Bol axioms for 1-lines and 2-lines, respectively, imply the inverse property. Hence they also imply (12). On the other hand, (9) and (12) together imply the identity

$$(13) \qquad\qquad [(xy)x]z = x[y(xz)].$$

The latter, which must not be confused with (9), clearly implies (12) and hence (9). But, more surprisingly, (13) is equivalent to each of the following (see [*S*VII Lemma 3.1]):

$$(14) \qquad\qquad z[x(yx)] = [(zx)y]x,$$

$$(15) \qquad\qquad (xy)(zx) = [x(yz)]x.$$

The equivalent identities (13), (14), (15) are known as the *Moufang* identities and characterize the class of *Moufang* loops. It should be clear from our discussion that a loop G is Moufang if and only if the 3-net defined by G is a Bol net.

Let us consider for a moment a phenomenon first noted by Bol [*S*66]. As shown by Example 1 of [*S* p. 124], there exists a loop G which satisfies (9) but not (13). This phenomenon simply cannot occur in the subject of division rings (see the discussion in Bruck [10]). Indeed, if a division ring merely has the left inverse property, then it satisfies (9)—for an elementary proof see Hall [2]—and it also satisfies (13). The latter fact, however, involves a long, hard journey into abstract algebra.

Just to avoid any confusion at this point, let us remark that the (unique) totally symmetric loop of order 10 is an example of a loop with the inverse property which fails to satisfy either (9) or (10), let alone (13).

The theory of Moufang loops is already quite extensive (see [*S*VII], [*S*VIII], Paige [*S*355], Bruck [13, 14]) and we cannot discuss it here in any detail. We remark merely that many known theorems for groups have interesting analogues for Moufang loops.

Let us consider again the net N defined by a Moufang loop G. Considering the construction for the line $L + M$ in the case that L, M are i-lines ($i = 1, 2, 3$), we may verify that

(16) $(i, x) + (i, y) = (i, x + y),$ $i = 1, 2, 3,$

for all x, y in G, where, in view of (12), we write

(17) $x + y = xy^{-1}x$

for all x, y in G. The groupoid $(G, +)$ defined by (17) was introduced by the author and called the *core* of the Moufang loop. For the theory of the core see [SVII.5], Bruck [14]. Here we shall merely note the distributive laws

(18) $x(y + z) = xy + xz,$ $(y + z)x = yx + zx,$

which hold for all x, y, z in G.

Tits [12] seems to have discovered the concept of the core independently. He considers a Bol net N and (in essence) introduces an operation o on the lines of N. This is done as follows: If the lines L, M belong to distinct classes, L o M is the unique line (belonging to the remaining class of lines) which is concurrent with L and M. If L, M belong to the same class, L o M is the line we have designated as $L + M$. Thus (in our notation; Tits is more abstract and more elegant),

$$(1, x) \text{ o } (2, y) = (2, y) \text{ o } (1, x) = (3, xy),$$
$$(1, x) \text{ o } (3, y) = (3, y) \text{ o } (1, x) = (2, x^{-1}y),$$
$$(2, x) \text{ o } (3, y) = (3, y) \text{ o } (2, x) = (1, yx^{-1}),$$

and $(i, x) \text{ o } (i, y) = (i, x + y),$ $i = 1, 2, 3,$

for all x, y in the Moufang loop G. Tits gives a set of axioms characterizing the groupoids (N, o) defined by Bol nets N, and investigates some interesting connections with the theory of triality for 6-dimensional hyperquadrics over an arbitrary field.

We have attempted here merely to give the reader a taste of the connection between loop theory and geometry. More along these lines will be indicated in the exercises which follow. For further details, see Pickert [11].

Exercises

1. Draw the figure which states that every loop of a 3-net has the right inverse property (Moufang-Bol axiom for 2-lines). That is, using Fig. 2, take x, y (or P, Q) arbitrarily, solve geometrically for x^{-1} from the equation $xx^{-1} = 1$, and draw the figure which states that $(yx)x^{-1} = y$. (Compare the drawings in Bruck [10].)

2. Draw the figure which states that every loop of the 3-net is associative (the Reidemeister figure).

3. Draw the figure which states that every loop of the 3-net is commutative (Thomsen's triangle).

4. Draw the figure which states that $xy = 1$ implies $yx = 1$ in every loop of the 3-net (the hexagon).

5. Draw the figure which states that $x^2x = xx^2$ in every loop of the 3-net (the hexagon).

6. Prove that all the groups of a Reidemeister net (Exercise 2) are isomorphic.

7. Prove that if a 3-net N is a Thomsen net (Exercise 2), then N is a Reidemeister net (Exercise 2) and hence every loop of N is an abelian (i.e., commutative) group.

8. Prove that if N is a hexagonal net (Exercises 4, 5) and if G is a loop of N, then every element x of G generates an abelian group.

In another direction, the left and right inverse properties and the inverse property have been replaced in recent work by other types of "inverse" properties. In any loop G, define the *right-inverse mapping*, J, by

(19) $x(xJ) = 1$,   all x in G.

Then, of course, J is a permutation of G. (Note that, for a loop with the left or right inverse property, $xJ = x^{-1}$.) Since J is a permutation, J has an inverse, J^{-1}. On replacing x by xJ^{-1} in (19), we get

(20) $(xJ^{-1})x = 1$,   all x in G.

A loop G is said to have the *crossed-inverse* property if

(21) $(xy)(xJ) = y$

for all x, y in G. (Section 6, Exercise 2, discusses a crossed-inverse property loop of order 5 which does not have the left or right inverse property.) From (21), on multiplying both sides on the right by $(xy)J$, we get

$$(22) \qquad y[(xy)J] = xJ$$

for all x, y in G. Similarly, from (22) by (21), we get

$$(23) \qquad (xy)J = (xJ)(yJ)$$

for all x, y in G. In view of (23), *the right-inverse mapping J of a crossed-inverse property loop G is an automorphism of G.* (Of course, all positive and negative powers of J are also automorphisms of G.) From (23) in (22),

$$y[(xJ)(yJ)] = xJ,$$

and hence, on replacing x, y by yJ^{-1}, xJ^{-1}, respectively,

$$(24) \qquad (xJ^{-1})(yx) = y$$

for all x, y in G. It is easy to show, in similar fashion, that (24) implies (21). Hence (24), (21) are equivalent identities.

A loop G is said to have the *weak inverse property* if the equation (i) $(xy)z = 1$ implies the equation (ii) $x(yz) = 1$. Since (i) tells us that $z = (xy)J$ and (ii) tells us that $yz = xJ$, we see that *the loops with the weak inverse property are precisely those which satisfy the identity* (22). Replacing y by $(yx)J$ in (22), and using (22) on the new left-hand side, we get

$$(25) \qquad [(yx)J](yJ^2) = xJ$$

for all x, y in G. Replacing x by $(xy)J$ in (25) and using (22), we get

$$(26) \qquad (xJ^2)(yJ^2) = (xy)J^2$$

for all x, y in G. Hence: *J^2 is an automorphism of a weak inverse property loop.* (Note that a loop G with the left or right inverse property also has the weak inverse property; but then J^2 is the identity mapping of G.)

A loop G is said to have the *automorphic-inverse* property if J is an automorphism of G. Two paragraphs above, we showed that (21) implies both (22) and (23). We also showed that (22) and (23) together imply (24); and we remarked that (24) implies (21). This means the following: *a loop has the crossed-inverse property if and only if it has both the weak inverse property and the automorphic-inverse property.*

Weak inverse property loops were first studied in 1940 by Baer [S348]; crossed-inverse property loops in 1955 by Artzy [S56]; automorphic-inverse property loops in 1959 by Artzy [16]. Further material on crossed-inverse property loops is in Bruck [S75], Artzy [15]. The connections with net axioms are studied (algebraically) using the concept of isotopy in Artzy [16], Osborn [17]. In particular, Osborn studies (in effect) those 3-nets all of whose loops have the weak inverse property.

Now we are ready for some more exercises.

Exercises

9. Draw the figure which states that every loop of the 3-net has the crossed-inverse property.

10. Draw the figure which states that every loop of the 3-net has the automorphic-inverse property.

11. Draw the figure which states that every loop of the 3-net has the weak inverse property.

12. Prove that an Artzy net (Exercise 9) is the same as a Thomsen net (Exercise 7). (For algebraic proofs, see Artzy [16], Osborn [17].)

13. Construct a loop G with the weak inverse property which is neither associative nor Moufang but has the property that every loop isotopic to G is isomorphic to G. (Osborn [17]. Compare Exercise 6; see also [SIII.2], Bruck [14].)

9. NONASSOCIATIVE INTEGERS

Let us begin by recalling some familiar facts. If x is an element of a multiplicative semigroup (see Sec. 3), then $x^1 = x$, $x^2 = xx$ and, more generally, if n is a positive integer, x^n denotes the (unambiguous) result of multiplying together n x's. We also have

$$(27) \qquad\qquad x^{m+n} = x^m x^n, \qquad x^{mn} = (x^m)^n$$

for all positive integers m, n. In a group, (27) holds for all integers m, n, positive, negative, or zero.

By contrast, if G is a multiplicative groupoid, quasigroup, or loop, and if x is an element of G, the symbol x^n need not be well defined for $n > 2$. For example, if $n = 3$, the symbol x^3 should reasonably denote both of the products $(xx)x$ and $x(xx)$; but, unfortunately, these products are not necessarily the same. For this reason, if we wish to use "integers" as exponents in connection with elements of groupoids, we must be prepared to accept a new concept of "integer." As a matter of fact, there is a slightly different concept according to whether we wish to deal with groupoids, quasigroups, or loops. Here we shall consider only loops.

Henceforth in this section, let G be a loop. First we shall consider the set S of all single-valued mappings of G into G; and, since our object is to consider nonassociative integers as exponents, we shall think of the elements of S as exponents. Then an element, θ, of S is a function from G to G such that, for each x in G, x^θ is a uniquely defined element of G. We note that if G, for example, has order 5, then S has order 25. Indeed, for each of the 5 choices of x in G, we have 5 choices for the "image," x^θ, of x under a mapping θ.

The ordered *sum*, $\theta + \phi$, and the ordered *product*, $\theta\phi$, of two elements θ, ϕ of S are defined by

$$(28) \qquad x^{\theta+\phi} = (x^\theta)(x^\phi), \qquad x^{\theta\phi} = (x^\theta)^\phi$$

for all x in G. [By design, formulas (28) are completely analogous to formulas (27).] As usual, we define $\theta = \phi$ if and only if

$$x^\theta = x^\phi$$

for all x in G. Straightforward computations then show us that the system $(S, +, \cdot)$ satisfies the following axioms:

(I) $(S, +)$ *is a loop.*

(II) $(S, \cdot)$ *is a semigroup.*

(III) $\theta(\phi + \psi) = \theta\phi + \theta\psi$ *for all* θ, ϕ, ψ *in* S.

These are the axioms for an *associative left neofield* (see Bruck [*S75*].) We may remark that if (II) were weakened to

(II′) $(S, \cdot)$ is a groupoid,

then $(S, +, \cdot)$ would be merely a left neofield. The term "left" comes from the *left distributive law* (III). It is easy to give examples in which the *right distributive law*,

(IV) $(\phi + \psi)\theta = \phi\theta + \psi\theta$ *for all* θ, ϕ, ψ *in* S,

does not hold. In fact, (IV) will always be false if G is a noncommutative group.

Before we go on, we must define two important elements of S. First we have the *identity mapping*, 1, such that

(29) $x^1 = x$

for every x in G. Next we have the *zero mapping*, 0, such that

(30) $x^0 = 1 =$ the identity element of G

for every x in G. We wish to remark that the zero mapping is the identity element of the additive loop $(S, +)$.

Next we define the *logarithmetic*, $L(G)$, of G. (The name *logarithmetic* was first introduced by Etherington [18] in connection with linear nonassociative algebras.) Suppose that K is the subloop of $(S, +)$ generated by the identity mapping 1. That is: K is part (or all) of S, K contains 1, $(K, +)$ is a loop, and K is as small as possible consistent with these conditions. Then we define $L(G) = K$.

The first significant fact which may be proved is this: $(L(G), +, \cdot)$ *is an associative left neofield*. To give a proof, we must show that axioms (I), (II), (III) hold (with S replaced by $L(G)$). Now (I) certainly holds as a consequence of our definition of $L(G)$; and (III) holds for $L(G)$ since $L(G)$ is part of S. The proof of (II) is more difficult. To prove (II) we consider the set T consisting of every element ϕ of $L(G)$ with the property that $\theta\phi$ is in $L(G)$ whenever θ is in $L(G)$. We first note that T contains 1. Next we observe that if θ, ϕ_1, ϕ_2, ϕ_3 are in $L(G)$ and

(31) $\phi_1 + \phi_2 = \phi_3,$

then

(32) $\theta\phi_1 + \theta\phi_2 = \theta\phi_3$

by (III). If some two of ϕ_1, ϕ_2, ϕ_3 are in T, then the corresponding two of $\theta\phi_1$, $\theta\phi_2$, $\theta\phi_3$ are in $L(G)$ for every θ in $L(G)$. But then, by the definition of T, the remaining term in (32) must be in $L(G)$ for every θ in $L(G)$, and hence the corresponding term in (31) must be in T. This means that $(T, +)$ is a quasigroup. Taking $\phi_1 = \phi_3 = 1$ in (31), we deduce that 0 is in T. Hence, of course, $(T, +)$ is a loop. Since, in addition, T contains 1 and is part of $L(G)$, we conclude that $T = L(G)$. At this stage we know that $(L(G), \cdot)$ is a groupoid. However, multiplication is associative (since $L(G)$ is part of S) and hence (II) holds for $L(G)$.

Before we go on, let us consider a familiar special case: let G be an infinite multiplicative group generated by a single element x. (Thus G is a so-called infinite cyclic group.) In this case, the elements of G are simply the powers x^n where n ranges over all rational integers (positive, negative, or zero). Moreover, $x^m = x^n$ if and only if $m = n$. In addition, the equations (27) hold for all rational integers. As might be expected, $L(G)$ turns out in this case to be isomorphic (both with respect to addition and with respect to multiplication) with the so-called *ring* of rational integers.

The example of the last paragraph suggests that another special case might also prove interesting. Suppose that G is a multiplicative loop which is generated by a single element x and (beyond the fact that it has a single generator) has no properties which are not forced by the fact that it is a loop. (There is one and just one such loop G, aside from an isomorphism; G is known as the *free loop of rank one* and also as the *free monogenic loop;* for details, see [SI].) In this case we denote the logarithmetic, $L(G)$, of G by I and call I the *left neofield of nonassociative integers*.

The very definition of I makes it obvious that I can be used as a left neofield of exponents in connection with any loop whatsoever. It is unnecessary for us to establish the properties of I here, since an excellent expository article on the subject is already available (Evans [19]). Evans has developed a number of properties of nonassociative integers, notably the theory of primes and prime factorization, and has suggested several problems whose study is likely to prove rewarding.

Exercises

1. Show that if G is a totally symmetric loop of order at least two, the logarithmetic $L(G)$ consists of just two distinct elements, 0 and 1. Write down the addition and multiplication tables for $L(G)$.

2. Find the logarithmetics of the various loops of order n for $n \leq 5$.

10. ROOM'S DESIGNS

In recent years, statisticians have been much concerned with various combinatorial problems, which they call *designs*, for the purpose of finding convenient patterns with which to handle experimental data. Most of these designs (aside from orthogonal latin squares and finite geometries) have, so far as I know, little connection with loops or quasigroups. As we shall show here, a design recently proposed by T. G. Room [21] proves to be an exception.

By a *Room design of order* $2n$, where n is a positive integer, we shall mean an arrangement of $2n$ objects, say 0, 1, $\cdots$, $2n - 1$, in a square array of side $2n - 1$ with the following properties:

(i) *Each of the* $(2n - 1)^2$ *cells of the array either is empty or contains exactly two distinct objects.*

(ii) *Each horizontal row (and each vertical column) of cells contains each of the* $2n$ *objects exactly once.*

(iii) *Every two distinct objects occur together in exactly one cell.*

We regard two Room designs as identical if they have the same order and if corresponding cells contain the same (unordered) pair of objects.

Suppose that there exists a Room design of order $2n$ on the elements 0, 1, $\cdots$, $2n - 1$. Number the rows and columns of the array from 1 to $2n - 1$, beginning at the top and at the left, respectively. By (ii), 0 appears exactly once in each of the $2n - 1$ rows and $2n - 1$ columns; by (iii), 0 is paired exactly once with each of the elements 1, 2, $\cdots$, $2n - 1$. Consequently, by permut-

ing rows and permuting columns, if necessary, we can arrange that
the cell belonging to the ith row and ith column contains the pair
$0, i$, for $i = 1, 2, \cdots, 2n - 1$. When this is true, we shall call the
design *normalized*.

Given a normalized Room design of order $2n$, let G denote the
set of integers $1, 2, \cdots, 2n - 1$. We define two binary operations
r, c on G as follows:

(i) *if x, y are distinct elements of G, the pair x, y lies in row numbered xry, column numbered xcy.*
(ii) $xrx = x = xcx$ *for all x in G.*

It is easy to verify that each of (G, r), (G, c) is a commutative
idempotent quasigroup of order $2n - 1$. Moreover, the pair of
quasigroups satisfies the following *orthogonality conditions:*

(O.1) *If p is in G and if x, y are elements of G such that $xry =
xcy = p$, then $x = y = p$.*
(O.2) *If p, q are distinct elements of G, there is at most one unordered
pair x, y of elements of G such that $xry = p$, $xcy = q$.*

By a *Room pair of quasigroups* we mean a pair (G, r), (G, c) of
commutative, idempotent quasigroups satisfying the orthogonality
conditions (O.1), (O.2). It is easy to see that such a Room pair of
quasigroups of order $2n - 1$ (when the integers $1, 2, \cdots, 2n - 1$
are used as elements) uniquely determines a normalized Room
design of order $2n$. Indeed, we merely assign the pair $0, x$ to the
cell in row x, column x and, for $x \neq y$, assign the pair x, y to the
cell in row xry, column xcy. We leave it to the reader to verify the
conditions (i), (ii), (iii).

Now let (G, r), (G, c) be a Room pair of quasigroups of order
$2m - 1$ and let (H, r), (H, c) be a Room pair of quasigroups of
order $2n - 1$. We define the direct product of the two pairs as
the set $G \times H$ of all couples (g, h), g in G, h in H, with the operation r defined by

$$(g, h)r(g', h') = (grg', hrh'),$$

and with the operation c defined in the same manner. It is easy
to see that $(G \times H, r)$, $(G \times H, c)$ is a Room pair of quasigroups
of order $(2m - 1)(2n - 1)$. Thus *from two Room designs of or-*

ders 2m, 2n respectively may be defined a Room design of order $(2m - 1)(2n - 1) + 1$.

At this point the reader may want to try his hand at some exercises.

Exercises

1. Prove that a finite idempotent quasigroup must have odd order.

2. Prove that if A is an additive abelian group of finite odd order k, the groupoid (A, o), defined by $a \text{ o } b = (a + b)/2$ for all a, b in A, is a commutative idempotent quasigroup of order k. [Moreover, A satisfies the *self-distributive law:* $a \text{ o } (b \text{ o } c) = (a \text{ o } b) \text{ o } (a \text{ o } c)$ for all a, b, c in A.]

3. Determine all commutative idempotent quasigroups of orders 1, 3, 5, and 7. [There are six nonisomorphic ones of order 7.]

4. Prove that Room designs of orders 4 and 6 do not exist.

5. Find Room designs of orders 2 and 8.

6. Does there exist a Room design of order 10?

The answer to Exercise 6 seems to be unknown. Exercises 4 and 5 were handled by Room [21]. We observe that the existence of a Room design of order 8 implies the existence of Room designs of order $7^n + 1$ for each positive integer n—a fact which is not in the literature.

There exist Room designs of order $2 \cdot 4^m$ for every positive integer m (see Archibald and Johnson [22]). For those who are familiar with the theory of finite fields, the following is a simple proof of this result: Let F be a finite field of order 2^k, $k \geq 2$, and let G denote the set of nonzero elements of F. We define operations r, c on G as follows: $xrx = x = xcx$ for each x in G; and, if x, y are distinct elements of G,

$$xry = x + y, \qquad xcy = (x^{-1} + y^{-1})^{-1} = \frac{xy}{x + y}.$$

Since F has characteristic 2, it is easy to see that each of (G, r), (G, c) is an idempotent, totally symmetric quasigroup. [And, obviously, the two quasigroups are isomorphic.] We examine the orthogonality conditions as follows: let p, q be elements of G (not necessarily distinct) and consider the possibility of satisfying the pair of equations

$$(33) \qquad xry = p, \qquad xcy = q$$

by an unordered pair x, y of distinct elements of G. By (O.2), there should be at most one solution if $p \neq q$; by (O.1), there should be no solution if $p = q$. Setting $x = pX$, $y = pY$, $q = pt$, and using the assumption that x, y are distinct, we transform (33) into

$$(34) \qquad X + Y = 1, \qquad XY = t.$$

Since $2X = 0$ for every X in F, we note that (34) has no solution with $X = Y$. From the theory of quadratic equations, (34) can have at most one unordered solution X, Y, whatever may be the value of t; thus (O.2) is automatically satisfied. The case $p = q$ corresponds to the case $t = 1$; and, by (O.1), in this case (34) should have no solution X, Y. However, when we set $t = 1$ in (34) and eliminate Y, we get

$$(35) \qquad X^2 = X + 1.$$

We note that (35) holds precisely when X is an element of F of multiplicative order 3; that is, when $X \neq 1$ and $X^3 = 1$. If such an X exists and if $Y = X^2$, then $X + Y = 1 = XY$, so that (O.1) is violated. Hence (O.1) will be violated precisely when the field F has an element of multiplicative order 3. However, since F has order 2^k, the multiplicative group is cyclic of order $2^k - 1$. There will be an element of multiplicative order 3 precisely when 3 divides $2^k - 1$; that is, precisely when k is even. Thus, to satisfy (O.1), we must take k to be odd. Setting $k = 2m + 1$, where m is a positive integer, we get $2^k = 2 \cdot 4^m$.

In the construction which we have presented, the members of the Room pair are isomorphic, totally symmetric, idempotent quasigroups of order congruent to 1 modulo 6. It is easy to see that the direct product of two Room pairs of this type will still be of the same type. These two facts should suggest some questions to the reader; if he asks and answers the right questions, he will get a real taste of mathematical research.

11. SUGGESTIONS FOR FURTHER READING

The most comprehensive exposition of loop theory now available is the author's book [S]. This, however, is written in a rather cramped style and may prove difficult for the inexperienced reader. An easier place to start would be with Bruck [S67], [S68], each of which is more leisurely, though somewhat out of date. In addition, each of these papers has something to say about totally symmetric quasigroups and loops, a topic omitted from [S], and [S68] has a detailed treatment of isotopy.

The best source for the connections between loop theory and geometry is Pickert [11]. This book, however, is written for the advanced student, and is also in German. A very imperfect substitute (which the student will find easier to read) is Bruck [10]. Other references, all of them quite technical, are Bates [S63], Bol [S66], Paige [S96], Baer [S348], Hughes [S353], and Tits [12]. The book by Hall [2] has a fine chapter on projective geometry but says very little about loops.

The inverse property for loops is treated in detail in [S]; the corresponding topic for quasigroups is in Bruck [S67]. We have already cited recent papers by Artzy [15, 16], Bruck [13, 14], and Osborn [17]. To these may be added Bruck and Paige [S76], Paige [S355], and Osborn [23].

There are very few papers on logarithmetics of loops; see Bruck [S75], Evans [19], and Etherington [24]. For logarithmetics of quasigroups, see a long series of papers by Mrs. Helen (Popova) Alderson (Popova [Sx], $99 \leq x \leq 105$, and forthcoming papers under the name of Alderson). As noted in Sec. 9, logarithmetics and free loops are closely related. For three different (but, of course, equally valid) accounts of the theory of free loops, see Bates [S63], Evans [S82], [S83], and Bruck [SI.3].

Here, perhaps, would be a good place to mention some of the broad topics of loop theory which we have omitted from the present paper: the theory of subloops, normal subloops, quotient loops, composition series, central series, direct decomposition. Before embarking on any of these topics, the reader would do well to read a good treatise on group theory (say Hall [2].) Then the corresponding theory for loops (in [S]) will be both meaningful and easily understood. Some of these topics, and others as well, are treated in the papers listed at the end of the present paper. It seems inappropriate, however, to refer in detail to papers dealing with topics which we have made no attempt to describe to the reader.

Although the present paper is ostensibly concerned with loops, quasigroups have come up at various points. Aside from the theory of free quasigroups, very little is said about quasigroups in [S], although the bibliography on quasigroups is probably complete through 1957. Two fairly comprehensive papers on quasigroups are Sade [S106] (this is largely bibliographical) and Stein [S358]. The paper by Frink [25] makes interesting reading but ignores the literature; the reader should be warned that the paper is largely expository. In recent years, the most prolific writer on quasigroups has been Sade; the reader who knows French will find most of Sade's papers an easy introduction to various topics on quasigroups. Rather than give references, we remind the reader of *Mathematical Reviews* (see Sec. 2).

APPENDIX

Our main aim in this appendix is to prove the known fact that there exists a Steiner triple system (see Sec. 5) of order n for each integer $n \geq 3$ such that $n \equiv 1$ or 3 mod 6. We shall also add some interesting constructions which are not needed for the proof.

The proof which follows is originally due to M. Reiss but has been simplified by Th. Skolem (see Netto [4]). The essence of the proof is to consider a certain property (P) of Steiner triple systems and to prove the following:

(I) *The Steiner triple system of order 3 has property (P).*

(II) *From a Steiner triple system of order n can be constructed a Steiner triple system of order $2n + 1$ with property (P).*

(III) *From a Steiner triple system of order $n > 3$ with property (P) can be constructed a Steiner triple system of order $2n - 5$ with property (P).*

Let us now see that (I), (II), (III) imply that if $n \equiv 1$ or $3 \mod 6$ and $n \geq 3$, there exists at least one Steiner triple system of order n with property (P). If $n = 3$, the proposition follows from (I); so we assume $n > 3$. Since $n \equiv 1$ or $3 \mod 6$, then $n \equiv 1, 3, 7$ or $9 \mod 12$. If $n \equiv 3$ or $7 \mod 12$, then $n = 2m + 1$ where $m \equiv 1$ or $3 \mod 6$ and $3 \leq m < n$. In this case, by (II), the proposition certainly holds for n if it holds for m. If $n \equiv 1$ or $9 \mod 12$, then $n = 2m - 5$ where $m \equiv 1$ or $3 \mod 6$ and $7 \leq m < n$. In this case, by (III), the proposition holds for n if it holds for m. Consequently there can be no n (subject to the stated restrictions) for which the proposition is false; and therefore the proposition is true for every n.

Next we must discuss the property (P). If $n \equiv 1$ or $3 \mod 6$ and $n \geq 3$, we may write $n = 2m + 3$ where m is a nonnegative integer. A Steiner triple system S of order n will be said to have property (P), the *periodic* property, if there exist three distinct elements p, q, u of S, forming a triple of S, such that the remaining $2m$ elements of S (if $m > 0$) can be given a circular ordering, say

$$(36) \qquad a_1, a_2, \cdots, a_{2m}, a_1, a_2, \cdots,$$

with the property that the third member of the triple containing

$$a_i, a_{i+1} \qquad \text{(subscripts reduced mod } 2m)$$

is either p or q, depending on i. Equivalently, we may suppose that

$$(37) \qquad p, a_{2i-1}, a_{2i} \quad \text{and} \quad q, a_{2i}, a_{2i+1}$$

are triples of S for each choice of $i \mod m$.

Since the Steiner triple system of order $n = 3$ may be supposed to consist of the single triple p, q, u, (I) holds trivially.

To prove (II), let S be any Steiner triple system of order n (not necessarily with property (P)). We know already how to construct from S a Steiner triple system T of order $2n + 1$ (by the methods of Sec. 5) but here we must construct T so that it has property (P). We do this as follows: Since $n \geq 3$ and n is odd, then $n = 2m - 1$ where m is a positive integer. Let $1, 2, \cdots, 2m - 1$ be the elements of S. Adjoin $2m$ new elements a, $b_1, b_2, \cdots, b_{2m-1}$, making $2n + 1$ elements in all. Define the triples of T to be:

(i) the triples of S;

(ii) the triples i, a, b_j such that $i - 1 \equiv 2j \bmod 2m - 1$;

(iii) the triples i, b_j, b_k such that $j < k$ and

$$i - 1 \equiv j + k \bmod 2m - 1.$$

(In each case, i, j, k are in the range $1, 2, \cdots, 2m - 1$.) It is easy to check that T is a Steiner triple system. To see that T has property (P), take $p = b_1, q = b_2$, so that $u = 4$. Here $2n + 1 - 3 = 4m - 4$. Since $b_1, a, 3$ is a triple, we may take $a_1 = a, a_2 = 3$. Suppose that, for some i such that $1 \leq i \leq 2m - 3$, we have $a_{2i} \equiv 4 - i \bmod 2m - 1$ (as is true for $i = 1$). Then, following the scheme of (37), we get

$$a_{2i+1} = b_{1-i}, \qquad a_{2i+2} \equiv 3 - i \bmod 2m - 1$$

(where $1 - i$ is to be made positive mod $2m - 1$). Hence

$$a_1 = a, \quad a_{2i} \equiv 4 - i \bmod 2m - 1, \quad a_{2i+1} = b_{1-i}$$

for all i such that $1 \leq i \leq 2m - 3$, and also

$$a_{4m-4} = 5.$$

If, finally, we notice that $b_2, 5, a$ is a triple, we have completed the proof of (II).

To prove (III), let S be a Steiner triple system of order $n > 3$ with property (P). We write $n = 2m + 3$ where m is a positive integer, and we assume (36), (37). We construct a Steiner triple system T of order $2n - 5 = 4m + 1$ as follows: We use $2m + 1$ of the elements of S, namely $u, a_1, \cdots, a_{2m}$, and $2m$ new elements $b_1, \cdots, b_{2m}$. The triples of T are as follows:

(α) the triples of S formed from three of the elements

$$u, a_1, \cdots, a_{2m};$$

(β) the triples b_i, a_i, a_{i+1} for $1 \leq i \leq 2m$;

(γ) the triples a_i, b_j, b_k such that $1 \leq i, j, k \leq 2m$ and either

(γ.1) $1 \leq j < k \leq 2m - 1$ and $i - 1 \equiv j + k \bmod 2m + 1$,

or

(γ.2) $k = 2m$ and $2j \equiv i - 1 \bmod 2m + 1$;

(δ) the triples u, b_j, b_k such that $1 \leq j, k \leq 2m$ and either
    (δ.1) $1 \leq j < k \leq 2m - 1$ and $2m \equiv j + k \bmod 2m + 1$, or
    (δ.2) $k = 2m$ and $2j \equiv 2m \bmod 2m + 1$.

Again it is easy to check that T is a Steiner triple system. To verify that T has property (P) we must arrange the elements as $P, Q, U, A_1, A_2, \cdots, A_{4m-2}$ so that a property analogous to (37) holds. We take $P = b_1$, $Q = b_2$, $U = a_4$. Since b_1, a_1, a_2 is a triple, we may start with $A_1 = a_1$. Then we find that

$$A_1 = a_1, \qquad A_2 = a_2, \qquad A_3 = a_3, \qquad A_4 = b_{2m},$$

$$A_{2i+1} = a_{i+3}, \qquad A_{2i+2} = b_{i+1} \qquad (2 \leq i \leq 2m - 3),$$

$$A_{4m-3} = u, \qquad A_{4m-2} = b_{2m-1}.$$

Since b_2, b_{2m-1}, a_1 is a triple, the proof of (III) is complete.

At this stage we have shown the existence of at least one Steiner triple system of order n for each $n \geq 3$ such that $n \equiv 1$ or $3 \bmod 6$. Now we shall consider another type of construction which abstracts and generalizes several types of construction discussed in Netto [4] and Carmichael [5]. It will lend interest to the discussion if we reconsider the existence problem and see how far the new method takes us towards its solution.

To begin with, suppose there exists an abelian group A of order n (written additively, with the *zero*, 0, as its identity element) which possesses a permutation ϕ such that

(a) $0\phi = 0$,
(b) $a\phi^2 = a$ for each a in A,
(c) $a\phi - (-a)\phi = a$ for each a in A.

We define a new operation o on A by the definition

(38) $\qquad\qquad a \text{ o } b = a + (b - a)\phi, \qquad$ all a, b in A.

By (a), we have $a \text{ o } a = a$ for all a; by (c), we have $a \text{ o } a = b \text{ o } a$ for all a, b; and, by (b), we have $a \text{ o } (a \text{ o } b) = b$ for all a, b. These three facts make it easy to prove that (A, o) is an idempotent totally symmetric quasigroup. Hence we have a Steiner triple system of order n. [We note that, for each element k in A, the mapping $a \longrightarrow a + k$ is an automorphism of (A, o) which sends 0 into k. Indeed, every idempotent totally symmetric quasigroup which possesses a transitive and regular abelian group of automorphisms can be obtained by such a construction.]

We may use the new method for the case that $n \equiv 3 \bmod 6$. In this case, $n = 3m$ where m is an odd positive integer. Let A be the direct sum of the group Z_3 (of integers mod 3) and an additive abelian group X of order m; that is, A consists of all ordered pairs (i, x), i in Z_3, x in X, with addition defined by

$$(i, x) + (j, y) = (i + j, x + y).$$

Since the order m of X is odd, there corresponds to each x in X a unique element $x/2$, namely the solution y of $2y = x$. We define a mapping ϕ on A as follows:

$$(0, 0)\phi = (0, 0), \qquad (1, 0)\phi = (-1, 0), \qquad (-1, 0)\phi = (1, 0),$$

and, for $x \neq 0$,

$$(0, x)\phi = (1, x/2), \qquad (1, x)\phi = (0, 2x),$$
$$(-1, x)\phi = (-1, -x).$$

It is easy to verify that ϕ satisfies (a), (b), (c). Hence our new method produces a Steiner triple system of order $n \geq 3$ for every $n \equiv 3 \bmod 6$.

Next let us suppose that $n \equiv 7 \bmod 12$. Then $n = 2k + 1$ where $k \equiv 3 \bmod 6$. By the preceding paragraph, there exists a Steiner triple system of order k. Hence, by a construction given in Sec. 5, there exists a Steiner triple system of order $2k + 1 = n$. Henceforth we need only consider the case that $n \equiv 1 \bmod 12$ and $n > 1$.

Before proceeding, let us suppose that there exists an additive abelian group A, whose order n is prime to 6, possessing an automorphism θ such that

(39) $$a\theta^2 - a\theta + a = 0$$

for every a in A. Then we have

(40) $$a\theta^2 = a\theta - a, \quad a\theta^3 = -a, \quad a\theta^4 = -a\theta,$$
$$a\theta^5 = a - a\theta, \quad a\theta^6 = a.$$

If $a\theta^3 = a$, then $2a = 0$ and hence $a = 0$. If $a\theta^2 = a$, then $-a =$

$a\theta^3 = a\theta$ and hence, by (39), $3a = 0$; whence, again, $a = 0$. There-fore θ partitions the nonzero elements of A into cycles of length 6. If $a \neq 0$ and if $a\theta = b$, we see from (40) that the cycle determined by a is

$$a, b, b - a, -a, -b, a - b.$$

We define ϕ on this cycle in either of the following ways: (1) ϕ interchanges the elements of the pairs $a, b; b - a, -a; -b, a - b;$ (2) ϕ interchanges the elements of the pairs $a, a - b; -b, -a;$ $b - a, b$. If we make one of the choices (1), (2) for each cycle of length 6, and if, in addition, we define $0\phi = 0$, we may verify eas-ily that ϕ has properties (a), (b), (c). Hence the existence of θ en-sures the existence of ϕ.

It is easy to see that if A is the direct sum of abelian groups A_1, A_2 and if, for $i = 1, 2$, A_i possesses an automorphism θ_i with prop-erty (39), then A possesses an automorphism θ with property (39); indeed, we need only define

$$(a_1, a_2)\theta = (a_1\theta_1, a_2\theta_2)$$

for all a_i in A_i, $i = 1, 2$. Hence we shall assume now that n is a prime or a power of a prime, and that $n \equiv 1 \bmod 6$. There exists a field F of order n, and we shall take A to be the additive group of F. The nonzero elements of F form a multiplicative cyclic group of order $n - 1$. Since 6 divides $n - 1$, F contains an element s of multiplicative order 6. It follows at once that $s^3 = -1$ and thus that

$$s^2 - s + 1 = 0.$$

Hence, if we define θ by $a\theta = sa$, then θ will be an automorphism of A with property (39).

Now let us see how far we have come by our new method. If $n \geq 3$ and if $n \equiv 1 \bmod 6$ (in particular, if $n \equiv 1 \bmod 12$), then

$$n = e^2fg$$

where e, f, g are positive integers and (i) if $f > 1$, then f is either a prime of form $6m + 1$ or a product of distinct primes of form $6m + 1$; (ii) if $g > 1$, then g is a product of an *even* number of distinct primes of form $6k - 1$. The remarks of the preceding paragraph show that if $g = 1$, there exists an abelian group of order n with an automorphism θ satisfying (39). Consequently, since we may form direct products of idempotent totally symmetric quasigroups (see Sec. 5), the only remaining case of interest is that $n = pq$ where p, q are distinct primes such that $p \equiv q \equiv -1 \bmod 6$ and $pq \equiv 1 \bmod 12$. For this case our new method seems to fail, and we must fall back upon the original existence proof.

BIBLIOGRAPHY

(*Note.* As explained in Sec. 2, this bibliography merely supplements that in [1].)

1. Bruck, R. H., *A Survey of Binary Systems*. Berlin-Göttingen-Heidelberg: Springer-Verlag, 1958. *MR* 20, No. 76.

2. Hall, M., Jr., *The Theory of Groups*. New York: The Macmillan Company, 1959. *MR* 21, No. 1996.

3. Reiss, M., "Über eine Steinersche combinatorische Aufgabe," *Journal für die reine und angewandte Mathematik*, Vol. 56 (1859), pp. 326–344.

4. Netto, E., *Lehrbuch der Combinatorik*, 2nd ed. New York: Chelsea Publishing Co., 1958. *MR* 20, No. 1632.

5. Carmichael, R. D., *Groups of Finite Order*. New York: Dover Publications, Inc., *MR* 17, 823.

6. Fischer, R. A., and F. Yates, *Statistical Tables for Biological, Agricultural and Medical Research*. London: Oliver and Boyd, 1943. *MR* 5, 207.

7. Norton, H. W., "The 7×7 squares," *Annals of Eugenics*, Vol. 9 (1939), pp. 269–307. *MR* 1, 199.

8. Sade, A., "An omission in Norton's list of 7×7 squares," *Annals of Mathematical Statistics*, Vol. 22 (1951), pp. 306–307. *MR* 12, 665.

9. Hall, M., Jr., "Distinct representatives of subsets," *Bulletin of the American Mathematical Society*, Vol. 54 (1948), pp. 922–926. *MR* 10, 238.

10. Bruck, R. H., "Recent advances in the foundations of Euclidean plane geometry," *American Mathematical Monthly* Vol. 62, No. 7, II (Slaught Memorial Paper No. 4), (1955), pp. 2–17. *MR* 17, 400.

11. Pickert, G., *Projektive Ebenen.* Berlin-Göttingen-Heidelberg:Springer-Verlag, 1955. *MR* 17, 399.

12. Tits, J., "Sur la trialité et les algèbres d'octaves," *Académie Royale de Belgique, Bulletin de la Classe des Sciences,* (5), Vol. 44 (1958), pp. 332–350. *MR* 21, No. 2019.

13. Bruck, R. H., "Normal endomorphisms," *Illinois Journal of Mathematics,* Vol. 4 (1960), pp. 38–87. *MR* 22, No. 4794.

14. Bruck, R. H., "Some theorems on Moufang loops," *Mathematische Zeitschrift,* Vol. 73 (1960), pp. 59–78. *MR* 23, No. A3192.

15. Artzy, R., "Crossed-inverse and related loops," *Transactions of the American Mathematical Society,* Vol. 91 (1959), pp. 480–492. *MR* 21, No. 5688.

16. Artzy, R., "On automorphic-inverse properties in loops," *Proceedings of the American Mathematical Society,* Vol. 10 (1959), pp. 588–591. *MR* 21, No. 6397.

17. Osborn, J. M., "Loops with the weak inverse property," *Pacific Journal of Mathematics,* Vol. 10 (1960), pp. 295–304. *MR* 22, No. 2660.

18. Etherington, I. M. H., "Non-associative arithmetics," *Proceedings of the Royal Society of Edinburgh,* Vol. 62 (1949), pp. 442–453. *MR* 10, No. 677.

19. Evans, T., "Non-associative number theory," *American Mathematical Monthly,* Vol. 64 (1957), pp. 299–309. *MR* 20, No. 58.

20. Minc, H., "Theorems on non-associative number theory," *American Mathematical Monthly,* Vol. 66 (1959), pp. 486–488. *MR* 21, No. 3470.

21. Room, T. G., "A new type of magic square," *Mathematical Gazette,* Vol. 39 (1955), pp. 307.

22. Archbold, J. W., and N. L. Johnson, "A construction for Room's squares and an application in experimental design," *Annals of Mathematical Statistics,* Vol. 29 (1959), pp. 219–225.

23. Osborn, J. M., "A theorem on A-loops," *Proceedings of the American Mathematical Society,* Vol. 9 (1958), pp. 347–349. *MR* 20, No. 79.

24. Etherington, I. M. H., "Groupoids with additive endomorphisms," *American Mathematical Monthly,* Vol. 65 (1958), pp. 596–601. *MR* 20, No. 5816.

25. Frink, O., "Symmetric and self-distributive systems," *American Mathematical Monthly,* Vol. 62 (1955), pp. 697–707.

26. Bruck, R. H., "Finite nets, I. Numerical invariants," *Canadian Journal of Mathematics*, Vol. 3 (1951), pp. 94–107. *MR* 12, No. 580.

27. Costa, A. A., "Über die Fastgruppentheorie," Universidade de Lisboa, Revista da Faculdade de Ciências, (2) Vol. 5 (1956), pp. 265–328. *MR* 19, 389.

28. Belousov, V. D., "Derivation operations and associators in loops," *Matematicheskii Sbornik*, Vol. 45 (87) (1958), pp. 51–70 (Russian). *MR* 20, No. 80.

29. Hofmann, K. H., "Eine Bemerkung über die zentralen Untergruppen in zusammenhängenden topologischen Gruppen," *Archiv der Mathematik*, Vol. 9 (1958), pp. 33–38. *MR* 22, No. 1630.

30. Hofmann, K. H., "Topologische Loops," *Mathematische Zeitschrift*, Vol. 70 (1958), pp. 13–37. *MR* 21, No. 1362.

31. Ikuta, T., "A remark on a loop," Natural Science Reports of Liberal Arts and Science Faculty, Shizuoka University, Vol. 2 (1957), No. 1, pp. 1–14. *MR* 19, 1159.

32. Popova, H., "Logarithmetics of finite quasigroups, II," *Proceedings of the Edinburgh Mathematical Society*, (2) Vol. 9 (1956), pp. 109–115. *MR* 18, 379.

33. Sade, A., "Groupoïdes automorphes par le groupe cyclique," *Canadian Journal of Mathematics*, Vol. 9 (1957), pp. 321–335. *MR* 19, 389.

34. Sade, A., "Quelques remarques sur l'isomorphisme et l'automorphisme des quasigroupes," *Abhandlungen aus dem Mathematischen Seminar, Hamburg*, Vol. 22 (1958), pp. 84–91. *MR* 20, No. 77.

35. Sade, A., "Quasigroupes automorphes par le groupe linéaire et géométrie finie," *Journal für die reine und angewandte Mathematik*, Vol. 199 (1958), pp. 100–120. *MR* 20, No. 78.

36. Wall, D. W., "Subquasigroups of finite quasigroups," *Pacific Journal of Mathematics* Vol. 7 (1957), pp. 1711–1714. *MR* 19, 1158.

THE FOUR AND EIGHT SQUARE PROBLEM AND DIVISION ALGEBRAS

Charles W. Curtis

Mathematics is to a great extent the development of axiomatic systems. As a distinguished observer and contributor from outside the field described it, "mathematics is the science of skillful operations with concepts and rules invented just for this purpose" [25]. The mathematical concepts of today—groups, rings, fields, modules, topological groups, normed linear spaces, etc.—were not invented quite as capriciously, however, as the preceding statement suggests. These concepts in each case were developed at a certain stage in the investigation of deep and intriguing problems of a special nature, whose solutions often required formidable calculations and deductions which obscured the essential difficulties of the problems. The second stage in the study of the problems came when, because of their demonstrated importance and applications, their difficulties were sifted out one by one, the leading ideas were given sharp definitions, and at last the results were presented in the relentless axiomatic style which is characteristic of current mathematical papers.

Two problems which illustrate this evolutionary process are the subject of this paper, and we shall follow their lively history from the beginnings early in the nineteenth century. Our account overlaps to some extent with Dickson's report [11] in 1919 on the state of these ideas, but we shall have to note developments that have followed Dickson's paper, many of which were inspired by Dickson's own work.

1. COMPLEX NUMBERS, QUATERNIONS, AND CAYLEY NUMBERS

Since both problems center around the concept of a field, we shall begin with this idea.

DEFINITION: *A field is a mathematical system consisting of a set F together with two operations $(+, \cdot)$ on F, called addition and multiplication, such that the following conditions are satisfied:*

(a) *Properties of addition.* For all a, b, c in F, we have

$$a + (b + c) = (a + b) + c \quad \text{and} \quad a + b = b + a.$$

There is an element 0 in F such that $a + 0 = a$ for all a, and for each $a \in F$, there is an element $-a$ in F such that $a + (-a) = 0$.

(b) *Properties of multiplication.* For all a, b, c in F, we have

$$(ab)c = a(bc) \quad \text{and} \quad ab = ba.$$

The equations $ax = b$ and $xa = b$, $a \neq 0$, always possess solutions.

(c) *Distributive laws.* For all a, b, c in F, we have

$$a(b + c) = ab + ac, \qquad (b + c)a = ba + ca.$$

(d) There exist elements $a \neq 0$ in F.

A word or two is in order about how well the concept of a field was understood in the early part of the nineteenth century. The real number system had already served as the basis for the deep and original work of Newton, Lagrange, Laplace, Euler, and others, but its presentation as a complete ordered field was certainly not emphasized before Dedekind's paper [10] of 1888. Before Hamilton, the complex numbers were still somewhat mysterious, and the term "imaginary number" was still used with feeling. In 1830 Galois had published a definitive paper on finite fields and had written his celebrated description of the connection between the field generated by the roots of a polynomial equation and the associated group of automorphisms of the field [12, 6]. He had applied his general theory to the problem, already solved in a special case by Abel [1, 6, 20], of determining in general when an arbitrary polynomial equation was solvable by radicals. But Galois' brief notes and papers failed to make much of an impression for many years after his death, and the study of abstract fields as a branch of algebra did not begin until Steinitz's paper [22, 23] of 1910.

From these remarks it should be clear that in the 1840's, William Hamilton and Arthur Cayley had no reason to be impressed with the importance of the axioms for a field. Our story begins with them, and we start with some facts, familiar to both of them, concerning real and complex numbers. The real numbers may be identified with the points on a line, and have therefore an order relation $a < b$ which corresponds to the geometrical statement that one point is to the left of another. The numbers $a > 0$ are called *positive*, and the connection between the order relation and the operations of addition and multiplication is that the sum and product of positive numbers is positive, and that $a > 0$ if and only if $-a < 0$. For $a \neq 0$, $a^2 > 0$, a fact which is clear if $a > 0$, whereas if $a < 0$, $-a > 0$, and $a^2 = (-a)^2 > 0$. From these remarks we obtain

(1) $a_1^2 + a_2^2 + \cdots = 0$ *implies* $a_1 = a_2 = \cdots = 0$;

and

(2)   the equation $x^2 = b$, where $b < 0$, has no solution in the system of real numbers.

Cauchy, Gauss, and others were familiar with complex numbers, obtained by adding an imaginary solution i of the equation $x^2 = -1$ to the real numbers. Once this is done, the resulting system is still required to admit the operations of algebra, and therefore contains all expressions of the form

$$a + bi + ci^2 + \cdots ,$$

where $a, b, c, \cdots$ are real numbers. Since $i^2 = -1, i^3 = -i, i^4 = 1$, etc., all these expressions simplify to the form $A + Bi$ with A, B real numbers. Moreover, we have by direct calculation

$$(3) \quad \begin{aligned} (a + bi) + (c + di) &= (a + c) + (b + d)i, \\ (a + bi)(c + di) &= (ac - bd) + (ad + bc)i. \end{aligned}$$

Hamilton [13] realized that the complex numbers could be studied from the point of view of analytic geometry. As the points on the line correspond to individual real numbers, so the points in the plane correspond to ordered pairs of real numbers (a, b). Addition of points on the line or in the plane can be defined geometrically as the resultant composition of vectors:

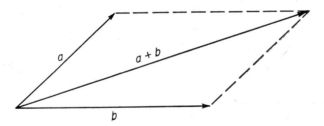

In the case of vectors on the real line, addition of vectors corresponds exactly to addition of numbers, while in the second case it is easily checked to be equivalent to

$$(a, b) + (c, d) = (a + c, b + d).$$

The geometrical meaning of multiplication is not so obvious, and in fact we state as our first major problem:

Problem 1. Given vector addition of points, is it possible to define multiplication of points in such a way that the resulting system is a field?

Hamilton observed that the formulas (3) made it easy to give an affirmative solution to Problem 1 for points in the plane. We define the complex numbers to be the set of all points (a, b), and set

$$(a, b) + (c, d) = (a + c, b + d),$$
$$(a, b)(c, d) = (ac - bd, ad + bc).$$

We can then verify that the axioms for a field are satisfied.

The next step was to observe that the complex numbers of the form $(a, 0)$ add and multiply according to the rules

$$(a, 0) + (b, 0) = (a + b, 0), \qquad (a, 0)(b, 0) = (ab, 0);$$

and we may say that these numbers form a *subfield* of the field of complex numbers which is *isomorphic* to the field of real numbers, and will write $a = (a, 0)$ so that we may think of the real numbers as a subset of the complex numbers. The mystery surrounding the solution of $x^2 = -1$ has now disappeared: we have $-1 = (-1, 0)$, and the equation $x^2 = -1$ has the solutions $(0, 1)$ and $(0, -1)$. More generally, we can verify that every complex number $z = (a, b)$ satisfies a quadratic equation with real coefficients

$$(4) \qquad X^2 - 2aX + a^2 + b^2 = 0.$$

The other solution of the equation (4) besides (a, b) turns out to be $(a, -b)$, which we shall denote by $\bar{z}$, and call $\bar{z}$ the conjugate of z. The product of the roots of (4) is equal to the constant term of the polynomial, and we have

$$z\bar{z} = a^2 + b^2.$$

The expression $a^2 + b^2$ has the geometrical interpretation as the square of the distance $||z||$ from the point (a, b) to the origin; thus we have

$$z\bar{z} = ||z||^2.$$

We may also check that

$$\overline{z_1 z_2} = \bar{z}_1 \bar{z}_2$$

for all complex numbers z_1 and z_2. It follows that

$$(5) \qquad ||z_1||^2 ||z_2||^2 = z_1 \bar{z}_1 z_2 \bar{z}_2 = z_1 z_2 \overline{z_1 z_2} = ||z_1 z_2||^2,$$

and if we set $z_1 = (a, b)$, $z_2 = (c, d)$, then we have the curious identity

(6) $\qquad (a^2 + b^2)(c^2 + d^2) = (ac - bd)^2 + (ad + bc)^2,$

which of course can be verified directly once we think of writing it down. The formula (6) asserts that a product of two sums of two squares can always be expressed as a sum of two squares.

With some reflection, we may formulate our second problem.

Problem 2. Can the product of two sums of n squares be expressed as a sum of n squares?

More precisely, we wish to find the values of n for which we have an identity

(7) $\qquad (a_1^2 + \cdots + a_n^2)(b_1^2 + \cdots + b_n^2) = A_1^2 + \cdots + A_n^2,$

where the A_i are given as bilinear forms in the a's and b's:

(8) $$A_i = \sum_{j,k=1}^{n} c_{ijk} a_j b_k,$$

with coefficients c_{ijk} which are independent of the a's and b's, where all the a's, b's, etc. are required to belong to a given field F.

The first problem can also be generalized as follows. Let F be a field, and let $V_n(F)$ be the set of all *points* $(a_1, \cdots, a_n)$ with coefficients in F. If we define the sum of two points by the rule

$$(a_1, \cdots, a_n) + (b_1, \cdots, b_n) = (a_1 + b_1, \cdots, a_n + b_n),$$

then the axioms for addition in a field hold. We then ask when it is possible to define a bilinear multiplication of points

$$(a_1, \cdots, a_n)(b_1, \cdots, b_n) = (A_1, \cdots, A_n),$$

such that the resulting system satisfies the axioms for a field. It is easily seen that a necessary condition is that the A_i be given by formulas (8), where the c_{ijk} are independent of the a's and b's.

Hamilton's major discovery [13] was that both problems have a solution for $n = 4$, when F is the field of real numbers. He defined

$$(a_1, a_2, a_3, a_4)(b_1, b_2, b_3, b_4) = (A_1, A_2, A_3, A_4),$$

where

$$A_1 = a_1b_1 - a_2b_2 - a_3b_3 - a_4b_4,$$
$$A_2 = a_1b_2 + a_2b_1 + a_3b_4 - a_4b_3,$$
(9)
$$A_3 = a_1b_3 - a_2b_4 + a_3b_1 + a_4b_2,$$
$$A_4 = a_1b_4 + a_2b_3 - a_3b_2 + a_4b_1.$$

Hamilton showed that all the axioms for a field are satisfied with the exception of the commutative law of multiplication. Such a system is now called a *skew field* or *division ring*. Hamilton's example was the first, and he called the objects *quaternions*. By analogy with complex numbers, Hamilton defined for each quaternion $q = (a_1, a_2, a_3, a_4)$ a *conjugate* quaternion $\bar{q} = (a_1, -a_2, -a_3, -a_4)$, and observed that

$$q\bar{q} = a_1^2 + a_2^2 + a_3^2 + a_4^2.$$

If we define

$$|q| = a_1^2 + a_2^2 + a_3^2 + a_4^2 = ||q||^2,$$

then we have

$$q\bar{q} = |q|,$$

and because a sum of squares of nonzero real numbers is not zero, we have $|q| \neq 0$ if $q \neq 0$. Then we obtain for the inverse of the quaternion $q \neq 0$,

$$q^{-1} = \frac{1}{|q|}\,\bar{q}.$$

We can also verify that

(10) $$\overline{q_1q_2} = \overline{q_2}\,\overline{q_1}.$$

As in the case of complex numbers, the quaternions of the form $(a, 0, 0, 0)$ may be identified with the real numbers, and we have

$$aq = qa$$

for all real numbers a and quaternions q. Now we are ready to derive a formula analogous to (6). We have

$$|q_1|\,|q_2| = q_1\overline{q_1}q_2\overline{q_2} = q_2(q_1\overline{q_1})\overline{q_2},$$

since $q_1\bar{q}_1$ is real, and hence commutes with q_2. Then by (10) and the associative law,

$$q_2(q_1\bar{q}_1)\bar{q}_2 = q_2q_1\overline{q_2q_1} = ||q_1q_2||^2 = |q_1q_2|.$$

Hence $$|q_1q_2| = |q_1|\,|q_2|.$$

Setting $q_1 = (a_1, a_2, a_3, a_4)$ and $q_2 = (b_1, b_2, b_3, b_4)$, we obtain the striking identity

(11)
$$(a_1^2 + a_2^2 + a_3^2 + a_4^2)(b_1^2 + b_2^2 + b_3^2 + b_4^2) = A_1^2 + A_2^2 + A_3^2 + A_4^2,$$

where A_1, A_2, A_3, A_4 are given by (9).

Euler [21, pp. 55, 198] had already observed the formula (11) in 1770, and had used it to prove the theorem of Lagrange which states that every positive integer is a sum of four squares. The formula (11) shows that because every positive integer is a product of prime numbers, it is sufficient to prove that every prime number is a sum of four squares.

Almost immediately after Hamilton's discovery, Cayley [9] found that both problems had a solution for $n = 8$. In the solution of Problem 1, however, both the associative and commutative laws of multiplication had to be abandoned. Specifically, Cayley demonstrated that Problem 2 had a solution for $n = 8$ by exhibiting a set of equations (8) for which the formula (7) holds. It follows from the bilinearity of A_1, A_2, $\cdots$, A_n that if we define

$$(a_1, \cdots, a_n)(b_1, \cdots, b_n) = (A_1, \cdots, A_n),$$

then we obtain a system satisfying the addition axioms and distributive laws of a field. Moreover, we have the additional property that if we define for $a = (a_1, \cdots, a_n)$,

$$|a| = a_1^2 + \cdots + a_n^2,$$

then

(12) $$|ab| = |a|\,|b|.$$

From (12) we see that $ab = 0$ implies $a = 0$ or $b = 0$. We now use the fact that the n-tuples with real coefficients form an n-dimensional vector space over the real field. Then the mappings $L_a: x \longrightarrow ax$ and $R_a: x \longrightarrow xa$ are linear transformations on this space whose null spaces consist of the zero vector alone, and are therefore invertible linear transformations on this space. Therefore the equations $ax = b$ and $xa = b$ can be solved whenever $a \neq 0$, and hence we have all the axioms for a field except the commutative and associative laws of multiplication. We shall call this algebraic system the *algebra of Cayley numbers*. A precise definition will be given in Sec. 3.

2. NONASSOCIATIVE ALGEBRAS

It is convenient at this point to introduce the following definitions.

1. DEFINITION: *A finite-dimensional vector space A over a field F is called a (nonassociative) algebra if there is defined on A a product ab which satisfies the conditions*

(a) $a(\xi b) = (\xi a)b = \xi(ab)$, $\xi \in F$, $a, b \in A$,
(b) $a(b + c) = ab + ac$, $(b + c)a = ba + ca$, $a, b, c \in A$.

We say that A is a *division algebra* if the equations $ax = b$ and $xa = b$ always possess solutions if $a \neq 0$. The algebra A is called an *associative algebra* if for all a, b, c in A we have

$$a(bc) = (ab)c.$$

Let $\{e_1, \cdots, e_n\}$ be a basis for the algebra A over F. Then every element $a \in A$ can be expressed uniquely in the form

$$a = a_1e_1 + \cdots + a_ne_n, \qquad a_i \in F.$$

We define the *norm* of a (with respect to the basis $e_1, \cdots, e_n$) by setting

$$|a| = a_1^2 + \cdots + a_n^2.$$

The algebra A is called a *normed algebra* if for some basis $\{e_1, \cdots, e_n\}$ the norm $|a|$ satisfies the condition

$$|ab| = |a| \, |b|$$

for all $a, b \in A$.

For any algebra A, the conditions (a) and (b) imply that the mappings L_a: $x \longrightarrow ax$ and R_a: $x \longrightarrow xa$ are linear transformations of the vector space A for all $a \in A$. We can now state a more precise version of the remark made at the end of Sec. 1.

2. *Any normed algebra over the field of real numbers is a division algebra.*

Proof: Since $|ab| = |a| \, |b|$, $ab = 0$ implies $|a| = 0$ or $|b| = 0$. Since $\Sigma_1^n a_i^2 = 0$ for real numbers $\{a_i\}$ implies that $a_1 = \cdots = a_n = 0$, we see that from $ab = 0$ we can conclude that $a = 0$ or $b = 0$. Therefore, the linear transformations L_a and R_a are invertible whenever $a \neq 0$, and it follows that when $a \neq 0$, the equations $xa = b$ and $ax = b$ can be solved. This completes the proof.

In terms of our new definitions, our original problems can be stated as follows.

Problem 1. Find all division algebras over the real field.

Problem 2. Find all normed algebras over the real field.

Indeed, the space of points $\{(a_1, \cdots, a_n)\}$ becomes an algebra if we define $(a_1, \cdots, a_n)(b_1, \cdots, b_n) = (A_1, \cdots, A_n)$ by the formula (8), and this algebra is a normed algebra if and only if the formula (7) holds.

We observe also that because of **2**, Problem 2 is a special case of Problem 1.

The half-century following Hamilton's and Cayley's discoveries saw many attempts to solve both problems. Because the known affirmative solutions of both problems occurred when the dimension of space was 1, 2, 4, or 8, the next case to try seemed to involve the 16-dimensional space over the reals. Several erroneous affirmative solutions of Problem 2 were given for the 16-dimensional space (see Dickson [11]). On the positive side, B. Peirce gave a precise definition of an associative algebra, and in 1878 Frobenius proved that the only *associative* division algebras over the real field were the complex numbers and the quaternions.

Finally, in 1898, a decisive solution to Problem 2 was given by Hurwitz [15, 11], who proved that a normed algebra over the field of real numbers could exist only for dimensions 1, 2, 4, and 8. The actual determination of all possible normed algebras, however, was not completed until recently, when A. A. Albert [4, 5] showed, that with slight variations permitted, the complex numbers, quaternions, and Cayley numbers were the only possible normed algebras over an arbitrary field of characteristic $\neq 2$. A solution of Hurwitz's problem based on a paper by Jacobson [16] is given in Sec. 3.

The first problem, on the existence of real division algebras, remained untouched well into the twentieth century, while evidence showing the special nature of the quaternions and Cayley numbers continued to accumulate.

First of all, Hamilton's insistence on the geometrical interpretation of quaternions received confirmation from modern topology. We observe that the group of rotations in the plane is isomorphic to the multiplicative group T of complex numbers of norm 1. Viewed as a topological space, the complex numbers of norm 1 form a connected, but not a simply connected, space, since there exists a simple closed curve in the space which cannot be continuously shrunk to a point. On the other hand, the additive group R of real numbers is a connected and simply connected space, and there is a homomorphism

(13) $$\theta \longrightarrow \cos \theta + i \sin \theta = f(\theta)$$

of the additive group R of real numbers onto the multiplicative group of complex numbers of norm 1. The fact that

$$f(\theta_1 + \theta_2) = f(\theta_1)f(\theta_2)$$

is equivalent to the addition formulas for the trigonometric functions. We may describe this situation by saying that the additive group of real numbers forms the *simply connected covering group* of the group of rotations in the plane.

In three dimensions, the situation is more complicated. Let us call a *pure quaternion* a quaternion x of the form $(0, b, c, d)$. The pure quaternions form a 3-dimensional euclidean vector space V in which the distance is given by

$$||x|| = \sqrt{b^2 + c^2 + d^2}.$$

The *group of rotations* G in this space is isomorphic to the group of linear transformations $T \colon V \longrightarrow V$ which preserve distance: $||Tx|| = ||x||$, $x \in V$, with the additional property that det $(T) = +1$. Viewed as a topological space, G again turns out to be connected but not simply connected. Now let $\tilde{G}$ be the multiplicative group of quaternions of norm 1. If $q \in \tilde{G}$, then $q^{-1} = \bar{q}$, by the formula preceding (10). It is easily checked that if $x \in V$ is a pure quaternion, then $qxq^{-1} \in V$ for all $q \in \tilde{G}$, and that the mapping

(14) $q \longrightarrow T_q \colon x \longrightarrow qxq^{-1}$

is a homomorphism of $\tilde{G}$ onto the rotation group G of the 3-dimensional space V, whose kernel is ± 1. Moreover, $\tilde{G}$ is topologically the set of all vectors (a, b, c, d) in a 4-dimensional euclidean space such that $a^2 + b^2 + c^2 + d^2 = 1$, and is a simply connected topological space. It has turned out that this idea of setting up the homomorphism (14) has provided physicists with an appropriate mathematical tool for describing the spinning electron, [24, pp. 182, 203] while as we pointed out, it provides in topology another example of a nonsimply connected topological group and its simply connected covering group.

The Cayley numbers have motivated what is still a flourishing branch of the theory of nonassociative algebras, namely the problem of classifying algebras in terms of identities which they satisfy. Cayley had observed that the Cayley numbers satisfied the identities

(15) $xy^2 = (xy)y, \qquad x^2y = x(xy),$

for all x and y. Viewed more abstractly, the Cayley numbers are a nonassociative algebra on which the "nonassociative polynomials"

$$f(x, y) = xy^2 - (xy)y \quad \text{and} \quad g(x, y) = x^2y - x(xy)$$

vanish identically. Algebras with this property are called *alternative algebras,* and one can ask whether the Cayley numbers are the only alternative algebras which do not satisfy the stronger *associative identity*

$$A(x, y, z) = x(yz) - (xy)z = 0.$$

In 1950, Bruck and Kleinfeld [7] proved that the only alternative division algebras which were not associative were the Cayley numbers. See the next article by Kleinfeld.

In this century, extensive work has been done on nonassociative algebras satisfying other identities. One of the most important types of algebras are the Lie algebras, which satisfy the identity

$$xx = 0$$

and the Jacobi identity

$$x(yz) + y(zx) + z(xy) = 0.$$

Lie algebras arise naturally in the following ways. First of all, let A be an associative algebra over F, and define a new product by setting

$$[xy] = xy - yx,$$

where xy is the associative product in A. Then it is easily checked that A is a Lie algebra relative to the new multiplication.

A second kind of example of Lie algebras occurs in the study of the *derivations* of an arbitrary nonassociative algebra A. A derivation D of A is a linear transformation $D: A \longrightarrow A$ such that

$$D(xy) = (Dx)y + x(Dy), \qquad x, y \in A.$$

For example, if A is a Lie algebra, the mapping D_x defined by $D_x y = xy$ is (because of the Jacobi identity) a derivation of A. The set of derivations $D(A)$ of A clearly forms a vector space over F, but the product $D_1 D_2$ of two derivations is not in general a derivation. It is not hard to show, however, that for $D_1, D_2 \in D(A)$,

$$[D_1 D_2] = D_1 D_2 - D_2 D_1$$

is always a derivation, and that the set of all derivations of A is a

Lie algebra, with respect to the bracket operation, called the *derivation algebra* of A.

The most important application of Lie algebras has been their use in the study of topological groups, where, for well-behaved groups, the set of one-parameter subgroups can be given the structure of a Lie algebra and used to study the group itself.

One of the basic problems in the theory of Lie algebras is the *classification problem*, in which we ask for a more or less explicit construction of all possible Lie algebras. A good place to begin is with the Lie algebras which cannot themselves be built up from smaller Lie algebras in any way. Since a single element and its scalar multiples always form a subalgebra of a Lie algebra, it is too much to assume that the algebra has no proper subalgebra. Instead, we assume that the algebra has no proper *ideals*, where an ideal in a Lie algebra L is a subspace L_1 such that $[LL_1] \subset L_1$. A Lie algebra L which has no proper ideals and such that $[LL] \neq 0$ is called a *simple* Lie algebra. Several examples of simple Lie algebras over the complex field have been known for a long time in connection with the study of the classical groups. These may be described as follows. Let V be a vector space over the complex field F, and let $L(V)$ be the Lie algebra of all linear transformations of V, with the multiplication given by

$$[TU] = TU - UT,$$

where TU denotes the usual product of the linear transformations. Let L_0 be the set of all linear transformations of trace zero; then it can be proved that L_0 is a simple Lie algebra. For the other examples, we recall that a function (x, y) which assigns to each pair of vectors x, y in V a complex number is called a *bilinear form* if

$$(\alpha x + \beta y, z) = \alpha(x, z) + \beta(y, z),$$
$$(x, \alpha y + \beta z) = \alpha(x, y) + \beta(x, z),$$

for all x, y, z in V and complex numbers α and β. The form is called *symmetric* if

$$(x, y) = (y, x), \qquad x, y \in V$$

and *skew symmetric* if

$$(x, y) = -(y, x), \qquad x, y \in V.$$

Finally, (x, y) is called *nondegenerate* if $(x, V) = 0$ implies $x = 0$ for all $x \in V$. Let (x, y) be a nondegenerate symmetric or skew-symmetric form on V. Then the set of all linear transformations T of V such that

$$(Tx, y) + (x, Ty) = 0$$

forms a simple Lie algebra. One of the great achievements of modern algebra is Elie Cartan's [8] proof that there are no simple Lie algebras over the complex field other than the ones we have listed, except for five *exceptional* Lie algebras of dimensions 14, 52, 78, 133, and 248. Every one of the exceptional simple Lie algebras has turned out to be intimately connected with the Cayley numbers, the smallest (of dimension 14) being the derivation algebra of the Cayley numbers.

Parallel to the theory of Lie algebras we have the Jordan algebras. See the article by Paige in this volume. These are nonassociative algebras in which the product $\{xy\}$ satisfies the identities

$$\{xy\} = \{yx\}$$
$$\{\{\{xx\}y\}x\} = \{xx\}\{yx\}.$$

Examples can be obtained from associative algebras if we define the new product $\{xy\}$ by

(16) $$\{xy\} = xy + yx.$$

As in the case of Lie algebras, the simple Jordan algebras over the complex field have been completely classified [17, 2, 3]. Apart from the analogues of the nonexceptional Lie algebras, there is only one exceptional Jordan algebra, of dimension 27, which cannot be constructed from associative algebras by the formula (16). Again this algebra can be constructed from the Cayley numbers. Thus in the theory of both Lie and Jordan algebras, the only "exceptional" algebras have arisen from the Cayley numbers.

All this time, Problem 1 remained untouched in its most general form. Surprisingly, perhaps, the first major progress on this problem did not come from algebra at all. In 1940 the Swiss algebraic topologist and geometer Heinz Hopf [14] proved by an ingenious application of the powerful new methods of algebraic topology that Problem 1 could have a solution only for n a power of 2. In 1957, again as a byproduct of more general investigations in algebraic topology, a solution to Problem 1 was finally achieved, independently, by M. Kervaire [18] and by R. Bott and J. Milnor [19], all basing their work on some general results of R. Bott. The result is that a nonassociative real division algebra can exist only in the cases discovered by Hamilton and Cayley, for $n = 1, 2, 4, 8$.

3. SOLUTION OF HURWITZ'S PROBLEM

Our purpose in this section is to prove that the only normed algebras over the real field are the complex numbers, quaternions, and the Cayley numbers. Our presentation is based on a recent paper of Jacobson [16] and includes constructions of the quaternions and Cayley numbers that are simpler than those sketched in Sec. 1. We shall consider only algebras over the real field F, so that our results are not quite as general as those in Jacobson's paper. It will be seen that the key to the whole problem is the systematic generalization of the construction described in Sec. 1 of the field of complex numbers. We begin with some necessary conditions. Let A be a normed algebra over F. Then for some basis $e_1, \cdots, e_n$, the norm function defined with respect to this basis by

$$(17) \qquad |a| = a_1^2 + \cdots + a_n^2$$

where $a = \Sigma\, a_i e_i$, has the property that

$$(18) \qquad |ab| = |a|\,|b|.$$

Our first observation is that there is no loss of generality in assuming that A has an identity element 1 such that $1a = a1 = a$ for all $a \in F$. In fact, because of (17) we can find $e \in A$ such that $|e| = 1$. Then we have $|ex| = |xe| = |x|$ for all $x \in A$. This relation implies that the left and right multiplications L_e and R_e are invertible linear transformations of A onto itself which preserve the norm. Therefore L_e^{-1} and R_e^{-1} are also norm preserving. We define a new product in A by setting

$$x \cdot y = (R_e^{-1}(x))(L_e^{-1}(y)),$$

and set $1 = e^2$. Then

$$\begin{aligned} 1 \cdot y = e^2 \cdot y &= R_e^{-1}(e^2)L_e^{-1}(y) = e(L_e^{-1}(y)) \\ &= L_e(L_e^{-1}(y)) = y, \qquad y \in A, \end{aligned}$$

and similarly $y \cdot 1 = y$ for all y. Moreover,

$$\begin{aligned} |x \cdot y| = |R_e^{-1}(x)L_e^{-1}(y)| &= |R_e^{-1}(x)|\,|L_e^{-1}(y)| \\ &= |x|\,|y|. \end{aligned}$$

Thus we may assume to begin with that A contains an element 1 such that $1x = x1 = x$ for all x.

In order to exploit the geometrical properties of the vector space A, we introduce the inner product

$$(a, b) = a_1 b_1 + \cdots + a_n b_n,$$

where $a = \Sigma\, a_i e_i$ and $b = \Sigma\, b_i e_i$. Then $|a| = (a, a)$, and

(19) $(a, b) = \frac{1}{2}[|a + b| - |a| - |b|], \qquad a, b \in A.$

We note that (a, b) is a nondegenerate symmetric bilinear form on the vector space A. Upon replacing a by $a + a'$ in (18) and using (19), we obtain

(20) $(ab, a'b) = (a, a')|b|.$

Upon replacing b by $b + b'$ in (20) and using (19) and (20), we have

(21) $(ab, a'b') + (ab', a'b) = 2(a, a')(b, b'),$

which also implies

(22) $(ab, ab') = |a|(b, b').$

We shall use the notation $[x]$ for the one-dimensional space spanned by a vector x; and for a subspace W of A, we denote by $W^\perp$ the set of all vectors $a \in A$ such that

$$(a, w) = 0$$

for all $w \in W$. Then it is immediate that for any subspace W of A,

$$A = W \oplus W^\perp,$$

that is every vector in A can be expressed uniquely as a sum of a vector in W and a vector in $W^\perp$.

In particular, $A = [1] \oplus [1]^\perp$. If we set $a' = 1$ and $a \in [1]^\perp$ in (21), we obtain

$$(23) \qquad (ab, b') + (ab', b) = 0$$

while if we take $b \in [1]^\perp$ and $b' = 1$, we have, by (21),

$$(24) \qquad (ab, a') + (a, a'b) = 0.$$

For any element $a \in A$, we can write

$$a = \xi \cdot 1 + b, \qquad \xi \in F, b \in [1]^\perp.$$

Then, by analogy with complex numbers, define

$$\bar{a} = \xi \cdot 1 - b.$$

Evidently $a \longrightarrow \bar{a}$ is a linear mapping of A into A such that $\bar{\bar{a}} = a$ for all a. Now consider (23), which holds if $a \in [1]^\perp$. On the other hand, we have for all $\xi \in F$,

$$((\xi \cdot 1)b, b') - (b, (\xi \cdot 1)b') = 0.$$

Adding this equation to (23), we obtain

$$(25) \qquad (ab, b') = (b, \bar{a}b'), \qquad a \in A,$$

while from (24) we obtain

$$(26) \qquad (ab, a') = (a, a'\bar{b}), \qquad b \in A.$$

From these equations, we have

$$(ab, b') = (b, \bar{a}b') = (b\bar{b}', \bar{a}) = (\bar{b}', \bar{b}\, \bar{a})$$

for all a, b, b' in A. Setting $a = 1$, we have

$$(b, b') = (\bar{b}', \bar{b})$$

and hence

$$(ab, b') = (\overline{b}', \overline{ab})$$

as well. Therefore

$$(\overline{b}', \overline{b}\,\overline{a}) = (\overline{b}', \overline{ab})$$

for all a, b, b' in A, and since (x, y) is nondegenerate, we have

(27) $$\overline{b}\,\overline{a} = \overline{ab}, \qquad a, b \in A,$$

and the mapping $a \longrightarrow \overline{a}$ is an *involution* in A. The space of elements left fixed by the involution is contained in [1], hence

$$a\overline{a} = \xi \cdot 1$$

for some $\xi \in F$. Then we have, since $(1, 1) = |1| = 1$,

$$\xi = (\xi \cdot 1, 1) = (a\overline{a}, 1) = (a, a) = |a|,$$

and hence

(28) $$a\overline{a} = |a| \cdot 1$$

for all $a \in A$. Similarly, $\overline{a}a = |a| \cdot 1$. We have also $a + \overline{a} = T(a) \cdot 1$, where $a \longrightarrow T(a)$ is a linear function on A.

Our last necessary condition is that A satisfy the *alternative law*

(29) $$a^2 b = a(ab), \quad ab^2 = (ab)b, \qquad a, b \in A.$$

We have

$$(ax, ab) = (x, \overline{a}(ab))$$

and by (22),

$$(ax, ab) = |a|(x, b) = (x, |a|b)$$
$$= (x, (\overline{a}a)b).$$

Because of the nondegeneracy of (x, y), we obtain

$$\overline{a}(ab) = (\overline{a}a)b, \qquad a, b \in A,$$

and similarly

$$a(b\overline{b}) = (ab)\overline{b}.$$

Since $a + \overline{a} \in [1]$, it follows easily that the alternative law (29) holds. Let us summarize our results so far.

3. *Let A be a normed algebra with an identity over the field F of real numbers. Then A is an alternative algebra with an involution $a \longrightarrow \bar{a}$ such that for all $a \in A$,*

$$a\bar{a} = |a| \cdot 1.$$

Moreover, $a + \bar{a} = T(a) \cdot 1$, where $T(a) \in F$, and for any $a \in A$ we have

$$a^2 - T(a) \cdot a + |a| = 0.$$

The space $[1]$ is the set of elements left fixed by the involution, while $[1]^\perp$ is the set of elements a such that $\bar{a} = -a$.

Now we shall prove a sort of converse to **3**, which is suggested by the way we proved the 2-square and 4-square identity in Sec. 1.

4. *Let A be an alternative algebra with an identity over the real field with an involution $a \longrightarrow \bar{a}$ such that for all $a \in A$,*

$$a\bar{a} = |a| \cdot 1, \qquad a + \bar{a} = T(a) \cdot 1, \qquad T(a) \in F.$$

Then

$$|ab| = |a| \, |b|, \qquad a, b \in A.$$

Proof: If we attempt to use the argument we gave for quaternions, we see that it breaks down unless A is associative. Therefore we must obtain some further consequences of the alternative laws. For this purpose we introduce the associator

$$A(a, b, c) = (ab)c - a(bc)$$

and note that the alternative law is equivalent to the assertions

(30) $$A(a, a, b) = 0, \qquad A(a, b, b) = 0.$$

Replacing a by $x + y$ in (30), we obtain

$$A(x, y, b) + A(y, x, b) = 0$$

and similarly,

$$A(x, y, b) + A(x, b, y) = 0.$$

Combining these relations, we have

(31) $$A(x, y, b) = A(b, x, y)$$

and

(32) $A(b, x, b) = 0,$ $x, b \in A.$

From (31) we have

(33) $x(yb) + (bx)y = (xy)b + b(xy).$

In (33) replace x by bx and y by yb, and add the resulting expressions to obtain

$$(34) \quad (bx)(yb) + (b(bx))y + x((yb)b) + (bx)(yb)$$
$$= ((bx)y)b + b((bx)y) + (x(yb))b + b(x(yb))$$
$$= b((bx)y + x(yb)) + ((bx)y + x(yb))b.$$

The latter expression can be computed using (33) and simplified if we note that because of (32)

$$b((xy)b) = (b(xy))b,$$

so that there is no ambiguity in denoting this expression by $b(xy)b$. Substituting (33) in (34) yields

$$(b^2x)y + 2(bx)(yb) + x(yb^2) = b^2(xy) + 2b(xy)b + (xy)b^2.$$

If we now replace b by b^2 in (33) and subtract the result from the previous expression, we obtain $2(bx)(yb) = 2b(xy)b$, which is the result we need. Thus we have shown that in every alternative algebra the Moufang identity

(35) $(bx)(yb) = b(xy)b$

is valid.

We can now prove 4. Because of the alternative law and the fact that $a + \bar{a} \in [1]$, we have the result that

$$(a\bar{a})b = a(\bar{a}b) \quad \text{and} \quad a(b\bar{b}) = (ab)\bar{b}$$

for all a and b. We obtain

$$|ab| \cdot 1 = (ab)(\bar{b}\,\bar{a}) = (ab)(\bar{b}(T(a) \cdot 1 - a))$$
$$= T(a)(ab)\bar{b} - (ab)(\bar{b}a)$$
$$= T(a)(a(b\bar{b})) - a(b\bar{b})a$$

$$= T(a)|b|a - |b|a^2$$
$$= |b|a(T(a) - a) = |b|a\bar{a} = |b||a|$$

as we wished to prove.

Now we are ready to construct all possible normed algebras. First let A be a normed algebra with 1, with involution $a \longrightarrow \bar{a}$, satisfying the conditions stated in **3**. We try to build a new normed algebra B from A by imitating the construction of the complex numbers. We introduce the vector space B of all ordered pairs (a, b), where $a, b \in A$, and define

$$(a, b)(c, d) = (ac - \bar{d}b, da + b\bar{c}).$$

Then B is an algebra with identity $1 = (1, 0)$, and if we set $j = (0, 1)$ then $j^2 = -1$, and every element can be expressed uniquely in the form $a + bj$, $a, b \in A$, where we identify $a \in A$ with the element $(a, 0)$ in B. Then the law of multiplication becomes

$$(a + bj)(c + dj) = ac - \bar{d}b + (da + b\bar{c})j.$$

It follows that B is associative if and only if A is commutative. For $x = a + bj$ we define

$$\bar{x} = \bar{a} - bj,$$

and verify that for $y = c + dj$ we have $\bar{\bar{x}} = x$ and

$$\overline{xy} = \bar{y}\,\bar{x},$$

so that $x \longrightarrow \bar{x}$ is an involution of B. We have also

$$x\bar{x} = (a + bj)(\bar{a} - bj)$$
$$= (a\bar{a} + \bar{b}b)1 = |x|1,$$

since $|x| = a\bar{a} + \bar{b}b$ for x in the vector space B. We have also

$$x + \bar{x} = a + \bar{a} = T(a)\cdot 1, \qquad T(a) \in F.$$

Now we determine under what conditions B is alternative. From **4** this will decide when B is a normed algebra. Since $x + \bar{x} \in [1]$, the alternative law

$$A(x, x, y) = A(y, x, x) = 0$$

is equivalent to

$$A(x, \overline{x}, y) = A(y, x, \overline{x}) = 0.$$

Since $\overline{A(y, x, \overline{x})} = -A(x, \overline{x}, \overline{y})$, these both reduce to the single condition

$$A(x, \overline{x}, y) = 0.$$

If $x = a + bj$, $y = c + dj$, then

$$\overline{x}y = (\overline{a}c + \overline{d}b) + (d\overline{a} - b\overline{c})j,$$

and

$$\begin{aligned}
x(\overline{x}y) &= a(\overline{a}c + \overline{d}b) - (a\overline{d} - c\overline{b})b + [(d\overline{a} - b\overline{c})a + b(\overline{c}a + \overline{b}d)]j \\
&= (|a| + |b|)(c + dj) - A(a, \overline{d}, b) - A(b, \overline{c}, a)j \\
&= (x\overline{x})y - A(a, \overline{d}, b) - A(b, \overline{c}, a)j.
\end{aligned}$$

Therefore B is alternative and hence a normed algebra if and only if A is associative.

We can now give examples of normed algebras.

(1) $A_1 = F \cdot 1$.

(2) $A_2 = (A_1, A_1)$, defined as in the preceding discussion. A_2 is simply the field of complex numbers.

(3) $A_3 = (A_2, A_2)$, defined as above. A_3 is the algebra of quaternions, and is associative since A_2 is commutative.

(4) $A_4 = (A_3, A_3)$, defined as before. A_4 is the algebra of Cayley numbers, and is alternative but not associative since A_3 is not commutative.

Here the construction stops, since the next algebra in the chain will not be alternative and hence not a normed algebra. It is our purpose now to prove that these examples exhaust all normed algebras.

5. THEOREM: *Let A be a normed algebra with an identity element over the field of real numbers. Then A is either the real field, the complex field, the quaternions, or the algebra of Cayley numbers.*

Proof: In this discussion, *subalgebra* will mean a subalgebra containing 1. Since $a + \overline{a} \in [1]$ for all a, any subalgebra is sent into itself by the involution $a \longrightarrow \bar{a}$. Let A_1 be a subalgebra of A. Then

$$A = A_1 \oplus A_1^{\perp}.$$

Suppose $A_1 \neq A$; then we can find $j \in A_1^{\perp}$ such that $|j| = 1$. Since $j \in [1]^{\perp}$, $\bar{j} = -j$ and $j^2 = -\bar{j}j = -1$. From the relation $x\bar{x} = |x| \cdot 1$, we obtain by replacing x by $x + y$

$$(36) \qquad x\bar{y} + y\bar{x} = 2(x, y) \cdot 1.$$

Applying (36) to $a \in A_1$ and to j, we obtain

$$aj = j\bar{a}.$$

If $a, b \in A_1$, then by (25)

$$(a, bj) = (\bar{b}a, j) = 0$$

so that $A_1 j \subset A_1^{\perp}$. We have also by (26)

$$(aj, bj) = ((aj)\bar{j}, b) = (a(j\bar{j}), b) = (a, b),$$

which proves that $a \longrightarrow aj$ is a 1–1 linear transformation. Hence A_1 and $A_1 j$ have the same dimension. From $a(\bar{a}x) = (a\bar{a})x = |a|x$, we obtain upon replacing a by $a + b$

$$a(\bar{b}x) + b(\bar{a}x) = 2(a, b)x.$$

If $a, x \in A$ and $b = j$, then this formula implies that

$$a(\bar{j}x) + j(\bar{a}x) = 0.$$

Since $\bar{j} = -j$, we obtain $a(jx) = j(\bar{a}x)$ and $a(\bar{x}j) = (\bar{x}a)j$. Therefore, we have

$$(37) \qquad a(bj) = (ba)j, \qquad a, b \in A_1.$$

Taking conjugates, we have

$$(38) \qquad (ja)b = j(ba).$$

Finally, from the Moufang identity (35) we have

$$(aj)(bj) = (j\bar{a})(bj) = j(\bar{a}b)j = (\bar{b}a)j^2,$$

and hence

$$(39) \qquad (aj)(bj) = -\bar{b}a.$$

The relations (37)–(39) show that $A_1 + A_1 j$ is a subalgebra of A which is obtained from A_1 by the construction we have given previously. Moreover, the involution acting in $A_1 + A_1 j$ gives

$$\overline{a + bj} = \bar{a} + \bar{j}\bar{b} = \bar{a} - j\bar{b} = \bar{a} - bj,$$

which was the involution we defined in our construction. We can now repeat the argument with A_1. Start with $F1 \subset A$. If $A \neq F1$, then A contains a subalgebra A_2 in our list. If $A \neq A_2$, then A contains A_3; if $A \neq A_3$, then $A \supset A_4$. We must then have $A = A_4$; otherwise A is not alternative, as we showed in our construction. This completes the proof of the theorem.

BIBLIOGRAPHY

1. Abel, N. H., *Oeuvres complètes*, Vol. I, pp. 28–33. Christiania, 1881.

2. Albert, A. A., "On Jordan algebras of linear transformations," *Transactions of the American Mathematical Society*, Vol. 59 (1946), pp. 524–555.

3. Albert, A. A., "A structure theory for Jordan algebras," *Annals of Mathematics*, Vol. 48 (1947), pp. 546–567.

4. Albert, A. A., "Quadratic forms permitting composition," *Annals of Mathematics*, Vol. 43 (1942), pp. 161–177.

5. Albert, A. A., "Absolute-valued algebraic algebras," *Bulletin of the American Mathematical Society*, Vol. 55 (1949), pp. 763–768.

6. Bell, E. T., *The Development of Mathematics*. New York: McGraw-Hill Book Co., 1940.

7. Bruck, R. H., and E. Kleinfeld, "The structure of alternative division rings," *Proceedings of the American Mathematical Society*, Vol. 2 (1951), pp. 878–890.

8. Cartan, E., *Sur la structure des groupes de transformations finis et continus*. Paris: Thèse, 1894; 2nd ed., Paris: Viubert, 1933. *Oeuvres complètes*, Partie 1, Vol. 1. Paris, 1952.

9. Cayley, A., "On Jacobi's elliptic functions, in reply to the Rev. Brice Bronwin and on quaternions," *Philosophical Magazine and Journal of Science*, Vol. 3 (1845), pp. 210–213.

10. Dedekind, R., "Was sind und was sollen die Zahlen," *Gesammelte mathematische Werke*, vol. III. Braunschweig, 1930.

11. Dickson, L. E., "On quaternions and their generalization and the history of the eight square theorem," *Annals of Mathematics*, Vol. 20 (1919), pp. 155–171.

12. Galois, E., *Oeuvres mathématiques*. Paris, 1897.

13. Hamilton, W. R., *Lectures on quaternions*. Dublin, 1853.

14. Hopf, H., "Ein topologischer Beitrag zur reelen Algebra," Commentarii Mathematici Helvetici, Vol. 13 (1940), pp. 219–239.

15. Hurwitz, A., "Über die Composition der quadratischen Formen von beliebig vielen Variabeln," *Nachrichten von der königlichen Gesellschaft der Wissenschaften in Göttingen* (1898), pp. 309–316; *Mathematische Werke*, Vol. II, pp. 565–571. Basel, 1932.

16. Jacobson, N., "Composition algebras and their automorphisms," *Rendiconti del Circolo Matematico di Palermo*, Vol. 7 (1958), Ser. 11, pp. 55–80.

17. Jordan, P., J. von Neumann, and E. Wigner, "On an algebraic generalization of the quantum-mechanical formalism," *Annals of Mathematics*, Vol. 35 (1934), pp. 29–64.

18. Kervaire, M., "Non-parallelizability of the n sphere for $n > 7$," *Proceedings of the National Academy of Science of the United States*, Vol. 44 (1958), pp. 280–283.

19. Milnor, J., and R. Bott, "On the parallelizability of the spheres," *Bulletin of the American Mathematical Society*, Vol. 64 (1958), pp. 87–89.

20. Ore, O., *Niels Hendrik Abel, Mathematician Extraordinary*. Minneapolis: University of Minnesota Press, 1957.

21. Rademacher, H., and O. Topelitz, *The Enjoyment of Mathematics*. Princeton: Princeton University Press, 1956.

22. Steinitz, E., "Algebraische Theorie der Körper," *Journal für Mathematik*, Vol. 137 (1910), pp. 167–309.

23. Steinitz, E., *Algebraische Theorie der Körper*. New York: Chelsea Publishing Company, 1950.

24. Weyl, H., *The Theory of Groups and Quantum Mechanics*. New York: Dover Publications, Inc.

25. Wigner, E. P., "The unreasonable effectiveness of mathematics in the natural sciences," *Communications on Pure and Applied Mathematics*, Vol. 13 (1960), pp. 1–14.

A CHARACTERIZATION OF THE CAYLEY NUMBERS†

Erwin Kleinfeld

1. INTRODUCTION

The subject of alternative rings might be said to begin and end with the Cayley numbers because alternative rings were defined in order to study the Cayley numbers, which in turn are the only distinguished members of that class.

Cayley numbers first appeared in print in 1845 [6]. They were not called Cayley numbers then, nor even "C" numbers, and we will not define them until they actually appear in the classification of alternative division rings in Sec. 4. Suffice it to say at this point that the Cayley numbers are extensions of previously known algebras such as the quaternions and complex and real numbers and that they share many of their properties, with one notable exception: multiplication in general need not be associative. In

† This work was supported in part by a grant from the Office of Ordnance Research.

other words, there exist Cayley numbers x, y, and z such that $(xy)z \neq x(yz)$. The question of whether such a system should still be called a *ring* is subject to diverse opinion, but one might justify calling it a ring because multiplication is very nearly associative. In fact, any subsystem generated by two elements has associative multiplication [5].

This paper's *raison d'être* is a constructive, self-contained proof that *alternative division rings of characteristic not two are either Cayley-Dickson division algebras or associative division rings*. Although the theorem is still true without restricting the characteristic, the Cayley numbers themselves behave differently in that instance and it seems undesirable to combine the two proofs. However, a very similar argument holds in that case [16]. Aside from characterizing the Cayley numbers, this result has had important applications to the study of non-Desarguesian projective planes. Suggestions for further reading on these and other connections involving alternative rings are given in Sec. 5.

2. DEFINITIONS AND PRELIMINARY CALCULATIONS

The *associator* (x, y, z) is a linear function designed to measure the amount by which three elements x, y, z miss obeying the associative law of multiplication. In the light of this, we define

$$(x, y, z) = (xy)z - x(yz).$$

Similarly, the *commutator* (x, y) is defined by $(x, y) = xy - yx$. Following Zorn [32], a ring R is defined to be alternative in case

$$(1) \qquad (x, y, y) = 0 = (y, y, x),$$

for all elements x, y of R. R is called a *division ring* if it has a non-zero element and the equations $ax = b$ and $ya = b$ have unique solutions for x and y whenever $a \neq 0$. Initially it is surprising that the very definition of an alternative ring should have such interesting consequences. For instance, would you say that any subring of an alternative ring that is generated by two elements must be associative? Or would you suspect that $((w, x)^4, y, z) = 0$ holds for arbitrary elements w, x, y, z of an alternative ring? The answer to both questions turns out to be *yes* and the structure theory of alternative rings is based on these facts. Yet these results do not lie on the surface; they are reached only after extensive experimentation with various identities. In these pages only the main road will be visible, and there are many hidden byways with no apparent destination. Do not expect an answer to why the road seems to bend one way and then another, for this would take us far afield from our objective—*to classify alternative division rings.*

Throughout this section we will deal with an arbitrary alternative ring R having arbitrary elements w, x, y, and z.

LEMMA 1: *The associator (x, y, z) is skew symmetric in its three variables and vanishes whenever two of the variables coincide.*

Proof: Since $(x, y + z, y + z) = 0$ and $(y + z, y + z, x) = 0$ are consequences of (1), we see that

$$(x, y, z) + (x, z, y) = 0 \quad \text{and} \quad (z, y, x) + (y, z, x) = 0.$$

But then the associator is skew symmetric in its last two and also in its first two variables. Then

$$(x, y, z) = -(x, z, y) = (z, x, y) = -(z, y, x),$$

and hence (x, y, z) is skew symmetric. Since $(x, x, y) = 0$ follows from (1), the lemma is now established.

DEFINITION: *The function $f(w, x, y, z)$ is defined by the equation*

$$f(w, x, y, z) = (wx, y, z) - x(w, y, z) - (x, y, z)w.$$

In case you are puzzled by this peculiar definition, take comfort in the fact that something pleasant can be said about this function.

LEMMA 2: *The function $f(w, x, y, z)$ is skew symmetric and linear in its four variables and vanishes whenever any pair of its variables happen to be equal.*

Proof: That $f(w, x, y, z)$ should be linear follows from the definition of f and the linearity of the associator. That it should be skew symmetric is somewhat more surprising. In an arbitrary ring one can verify that

$$(2) \quad g(w, x, y, z) = (wx, y, z) - (w, xy, z) + (w, x, yz)$$
$$- w(x, y, z) - (w, x, y)z = 0,$$

merely by expanding all the associators and cancellation. Consequently,

$$-f(z, w, x, y) = g(w, x, y, z) - f(z, w, x, y)$$
$$= (wx, y, z) - (w, xy, z) + (w, x, yz) - w(x, y, z)$$
$$- (w, x, y)z - (zw, x, y) + w(z, x, y) + (w, x, y)z$$
$$= (wx, y, z) - (xy, z, w) + (yz, w, x) - (zw, x, y),$$

using Lemma 1. In other words, it follows that

$$-f(z, w, x, y) = (wx, y, z) - (xy, z, w) + (yz, w, x) - (zw, x, y).$$

A cyclic permutation on the letters w, x, y, z in the last identity changes the right-hand side to its negative and this yields information about $f(w, x, y, z)$. In fact, it shows that

$$f(w, x, y, z) = -f(z, w, x, y).$$

From the definition of f it follows that

$$f(w, x, y, y) = (wx, y, y) - x(w, y, y) - (x, y, y)w.$$

But then identity (1) may be used to show that $f(w, x, y, y) = 0$. Replacing y by $y + z$ leads to $f(w, x, y, z) = -f(w, x, z, y)$. Since the two permutations on four letters that we have employed generate the symmetric group, we have proved the skew symmetry of f, but $f(w, x, y, y) = 0$ has already been shown. This completes the proof of the lemma.

Lemmas 1 and 2 are used so often in this paper that referring to them by name becomes tiresome, especially while in the middle of a complicated identity. This will also be true of other identities as they are proved. The reader is advised to look back to previous results whenever expressions seem to vanish mysteriously.

The next three identities are direct consequences of Lemma 2 and we leave their verification as a simple exercise for the reader.

$$(3) \quad (x^2, y, z) = x(x, y, z) + (x, y, z)x,$$

(4) $(x, xy, z) = (x, y, xz) = (x, y, z)x,$

(5) $(x, yx, z) = (x, y, zx) = x(x, y, z).$

LEMMA 3: *If $u = (x, y, z)$ and $v = (x, y)$, then*

$$(u, x, y) = vu = -uv.$$

Proof: $(x^2, y, yz) = (x^2, y, z)y = (xu)y + (ux)y$, using in succession (4) and (3). At the same time,

$$(x^2, y, yz) = x(x, y, yz) + (x, y, yz)x = x(uy) + (uy)x,$$

using the same two identities but in reverse order. Comparison shows that $(xu)y + (ux)y = x(uy) + (uy)x$. Consequently,

$$(x, u, y) = (xu)y - x(uy) = (uy)x - (ux)y.$$

But

$$(uy)x - (ux)y = (u, y, x) + u(yx) - (u, x, y) - u(xy)$$
$$= -2(u, x, y) - uv.$$

Piecing together the various parts now shows that

$$(x, u, y) = -2(u, x, y) - uv.$$

Since $(x, u, y) = -(u, x, y)$ as a result of Lemma 1, it follows that $(u, x, y) = -uv$. A similar argument, starting with two expansions of (x^2, y, zy) leads to $(u, x, y) = vu$. This completes the proof of the lemma.

DEFINITION: *The nucleus N of R is defined as the set of all elements n in R such that $(n, R, R) = 0$. The center C of R consists of all elements c in N such that $(c, R) = 0$.*

It is easy to prove that N is a subring of R by making use of Lemma 2. Another identity that is of some use involves commutators and associators. Thus we may expand

$$(xy, z) - x(y, z) - (x, z)y = (xy)z - z(xy) - x(yz) + x(zy)$$
$$- (xz)y + (zx)y$$
$$= (x, y, z) - (x, z, y) + (z, x, y)$$
$$= 3(x, y, z).$$

We have established

(6) $(xy, z) - x(y, z) - (x, z)y = 3(x, y, z).$

Hence if x and y belong to C and z is an arbitrary element of R, then as a result of (6) we obtain $(xy, z) = 0$, whereas the definition of f implies $f(x, y, z, w) = 0$. Then C must be a subring of N.

Note that $N = R$ if and only if R is an associative ring and $C = R$ if and only if R is associative and commutative.

3. ELEMENTARY PROPERTIES OF DIVISION RINGS

In this section R will be assumed to denote an alternative division ring. R has the property that if $xy = 0$, then either $x = 0$ or $y = 0$. It can be shown now that R actually contains a unit element 1. Suppose that a is any nonzero element of R. Then there must exist an element b in R, $b \neq 0$, such that $ba = a$. Therefore,

$$b^2a = b(ba) = ba.$$

But then $(b^2 - b)a = 0$, so that $b^2 = b$. But then $0 = (b^2 - b)x = b(bx - x)$ and hence $bx = x$ for every x in R. Similarly, $0 = x(b^2 - b) = (xb - x)b$ and then $xb = x$. Then b must be the unit element 1 of R. If y satisfies $yx = 1$, then

$$0 = (x, y, x) = (xy)x - x = (xy - 1)x.$$

Since $x \neq 0$, it must be that $xy = 1$. Thus every $x \neq 0$ has a unique inverse, which we denote by x^{-1}. For arbitrary z in R,

$$(x, x^{-1}, z)x = (x, xx^{-1}, z) = (x, 1, z) = 0.$$

Therefore,

$$(x, x^{-1}, z) = 0.$$

We shall assume throughout that $1 + 1 \neq 0$. From this it follows that whenever $2x = 0$, since $(1 + 1)x = 0$, we must have $x = 0$. Now we are ready to establish some properties of the nucleus of an alternative division ring.

LEMMA 4: *Either $N = R$, or $N = C = $ field.*

Proof: Select arbitrary $n, n' \in N$, $w, x, y, z \in R$. Obviously,

$$f(x, y, z, n) = (xy, z, n) - y(x, z, n) - (y, z, n)x = 0.$$

Then from Lemma 2 it follows that $f(n, x, y, z) = 0$. But

$$f(n, x, y, z) = (nx, y, z) - x(n, y, z) - (x, y, z)n,$$

so that $(nx, y, z) = (x, y, z)n$. Similarly, $(xn, y, z) = n(x, y, z)$. As a consequence of (2),

$$\begin{aligned}
0 = g(x, n, y, z) &= (xn, y, z) - (x, ny, z) + (x, n, yz) \\
&\quad - x(n, y, z) - (x, n, y)z \\
&= (xn, y, z) - (x, ny, z).
\end{aligned}$$

But $(xn, y, z) = n(x, y, z)$, whereas

$$(x, ny, z) = (ny, z, x) = (y, z, x)n = (x, y, z)n.$$

Thus $n(x, y, z) = (x, y, z)n$ and also $((n, x), y, z) = 0$. The latter identity may be denoted by $((N, R), R, R) = 0$, so that $(N, R) \subset N$. Because of (6),

$$(wx, n) = w(x, n) + (w, n)x + 3(w, x, n) = w(x, n) + (w, n)x.$$

But then $0 = ((wx, n), y, z) = (w(x, n), y, z) + ((w, n)x, y, z)$. Since $(x, n), (w, n) \in N$, $(w(x, n), y, z) = (x, n)(w, y, z)$, and $((w, n)x, y, z) = (w, n)(x, y, z)$, we get

$$(x, n)(w, y, z) + (w, n)(x, y, z) = 0.$$

Since we are assuming $1 + 1 \neq 0$ anyway, a shortcut is possible at this point, for let $w = x$. Then $2(x, n)(x, y, z) = 0$. If $x \notin N$, then there always exist y, z such that $(x, y, z) \neq 0$, so that $(x, n) = 0$. On the other hand, let $w = n'$ above. In that case, $(n, n')(x, y, z) = 0$. Assuming $N \neq R$, then $(n, n') = 0$. Thus in either case $(R, n) = 0$, and hence $N = C$. Since $1 \in C$, $C \neq 0$. We have already seen that C is a subring of R and that C is associative and commutative. One needs only to show that for every $c \in C$, $c^{-1} \in C$ in order to finish the proof of the lemma and that simple task is left to the reader.

The significance of the following result will become apparent later.

LEMMA 5: *If $N \neq R$ and $(a, b, R) = 0$, then $(a, b) = 0$.*

Proof: Since $(a, b, R) = 0$, it follows that $f(a, b, R, R) = 0$, because

$$f(x, y, a, b) = (xy, a, b) - y(x, a, b) - (y, a, b)x = 0.$$

If r, s are arbitrary elements of R, then

$$
\begin{aligned}
0 &= g(a, b, r, s) + f(b, r, s, a) - f(b, a, r, s) \\
&= (ab, r, s) - (a, br, s) + (a, b, rs) - a(b, r, s) - (a, b, r)s \\
&\quad + (br, s, a) - r(b, s, a) - (r, s, a)b \\
&\quad - (ba, r, s) + a(b, r, s) + (a, r, s)b \\
&= ((a, b), r, s).
\end{aligned}
$$

Hence, $(a, b) \in N$. But since $(a, b, R) = 0$, it must also be true that $(a, ab, R) = 0$, because of (4). Then, using the same argument with ab substituted for b, it follows that $(a, ab) \in N$. But

$$(a, ab) = a(ab) - (ab)a = a(ab) - a(ba) = a(a, b).$$

In view of Lemma 4, $N = C$. Hence $(a(a, b), b) = 0$. On the other hand, (6) implies that $(a(a, b), b) = (a, b)^2$, since $(a, b) \in C$. Thus $(a, b)^2 = 0$. Since R is a division ring, it follows that $(a, b) = 0$. This completes the proof of the lemma.

The following result is a special case of the main theorem.

LEMMA 6: *If R is commutative, then it is associative and thus a field.*

Proof: Suppose $R \neq N$. Because of (3), $(x^2, x, R) = 0$. But then as before one can show that $f(x^2, x, R, R) = 0$. Then

$$
\begin{aligned}
(x^3, y, z) &= f(x^2, x, y, z) + x(x^2, y, z) + (x, y, z)x^2 \\
&= 2x \cdot x(x, y, z) + x^2(x, y, z),
\end{aligned}
$$

using commutativity together with (3). Since $x \cdot x(x, y, z) = x^2(x, y, z)$, we have shown that $(x^3, y, z) = 3x^2(x, y, z)$. On the other hand, identity (6) together with commutativity imply that $3(x, y, z) = 0$. Since $R \neq N$, it must follow that $3 = 0$. Conse-

134

quently we have $(x^3, y, z) = 0$, so that $x^3 \in N = C$ for all $x \in R$. If $a, b \in R$, then $(a - b)^3 = a^3 - b^3$ because of commutativity and the fact that $3 = 0$. Letting $a = (xy)z$ and $b = x(yz)$, it follows that

$$u^3 = [(xy)z]^3 - [x(yz)]^3 = (xy)^3 z^3 - x^3 (yz)^3$$
$$= (x^3 y^3) z^3 - x^3 (y^3 z^3) = 0,$$

since $x^3 \in N$. Thus we have shown that $u^3 = 0$, so that $u = 0$. But then $R = N$, contrary to assumption. This completes the proof of the lemma.

LEMMA 7: *If a, b, c, are pairwise anticommutative elements, then for every permutation σ of a, b, c*

(i) $\sigma(a) \cdot \sigma(b)\sigma(c) = \operatorname{sgn} \sigma(a \cdot bc)$,

(ii) $\sigma(a)\sigma(b) \cdot \sigma(c) = \operatorname{sgn} \sigma(ab \cdot c)$.

Proof: Since $(a, b, c) + (b, a, c) = 0$,

$$0 = (a, b, c) + (b, a, c) - (ab + ba)c$$
$$= (ab)c - a(bc) + (ba)c - b(ac) - (ab)c - (ba)c$$
$$= -a(bc) - b(ac).$$

Therefore, $a(bc) = -b(ac)$. This establishes (i). A similar computation leads to (ii). This completes the proof of the lemma.

LEMMA 8: *If $v = (x, y)$, then $v^2 \in N$.*

Proof: Substituting (x, z) for z in Lemma 3 shows that

$$v(x, y, (x, z)) + (x, y, (x, z))v = 0.$$

Also, $(x, y, (x, z)) = (x, (x, y), z) = (x, v, z)$, as a result of (4) and (5). But then $(x, v^2, z) = v(x, v, z) + (x, v, z)v = 0$, using (3). Since z can be replaced by an arbitrary product in the last identity, it follows that $f(v^2, x, R, R) = 0$. On the other hand, one may use this identity to break up

$$(v^2, xy, z) = -f(v^2, x, y, z) + y(v^2, x, z) + (v^2, y, z)x.$$

But each of the three terms is zero. Thus $(v^2, xy, z) = 0$. Again z may be replaced by an arbitrary product of two elements in the last identity so that $f(v^2, xy, R, R) = 0$ follows. For arbitrary elements $r, s \in R$,

$$(v^2, (x, r, y), s) = v(v, (x, r, y), s) + (v, (x, r, y), s)v$$
$$= (v, v(x, r, y) + (x, r, y)v, s),$$

employing (3), (4), and (5). But $v(x, r, y) + (x, r, y)v = 0$, as a consequence of Lemma 3, so that $(v^2, (x, r, y), s) = 0$. Now

$$(v^2, (xr)y, s) = -f(v^2, xr, y, s) + y(v^2, xr, s) + (v^2, y, s) \cdot xr$$
$$= y(v^2, xr, s)$$
$$= -yf(v^2, x, r, s) + y \cdot r(v^2, x, s) + y \cdot (v^2, r, s)x$$
$$= y \cdot (v^2, r, s)x.$$

Also,

$$(v^2, x(ry), s) = -f(v^2, x, ry, s) + ry \cdot (v^2, x, s) + (v^2, ry, s)x$$
$$= (v^2, ry, s)x = -f(v^2, r, y, s)x + y(v^2, r, s) \cdot x$$
$$+ (v^2, y, s)r \cdot x$$
$$= y(v^2, r, s) \cdot x.$$

Since $(v^2, (xr)y, s) = (v^2, x(ry), s)$ follows from above, it must be true that $y \cdot (v^2, r, s)x = y(v^2, r, s) \cdot x$. We may conclude that $((v^2, r, s), y, x) = 0$. Going back to the identity $(v^2, (x, r, y), s) = 0$, we observe that $(v^2, (x, y, r), s) = 0$. Now

$$(v^2, (xy)r, s) = -f(v^2, xy, r, s) + r(v^2, xy, s) + (v^2, r, s) \cdot xy$$
$$= (v^2, r, s) \cdot xy.$$

Also,

$$(v^2, x(yr), s) = -f(v^2, x, yr, s) + yr \cdot (v^2, x, s) + (v^2, yr, s)x$$
$$= (v^2, yr, s)x = -f(v^2, y, r, s)x + r(v^2, y, s) \cdot x$$
$$+ (v^2, r, s)y \cdot x$$
$$= (v^2, r, s)y \cdot x.$$

Therefore,

$$(v^2, r, s)y \cdot x = (v^2, r, s) \cdot xy.$$

But we have shown that $((v^2, r, s), y, x) = 0$. Hence

$$(v^2, r, s) \cdot xy = (v^2, r, s) \cdot yx.$$

This last identity is equivalent to $(v^2, r, s)\, v = 0$. Since R has no divisors of zero, it follows that either $v = 0$ or $(v^2, r, s) = 0$. Then in either case $(v^2, r, s) = 0$, so that $v^2 \in N$. This completes the proof of the lemma.

The observant reader will be able to carry out the proof of Lemma 8 one step further and show that in an arbitrary alternative ring, not necessarily a division ring, $v^4 \in N$.

LEMMA 9: *If $u = (x, y, z)$, then $u^2 \in N$.*

Proof: Let us assume that $v = (x, y) \neq 0$. Then $v^2 \in N$, and $(u, v)^2 \in N$, as a result of Lemma 8. Also, $uv + vu = 0$ follows from Lemma 3. But then $(u, v)^2 = (2uv)^2 = -4u^2v^2$. Since $-4v^2 \neq 0$, one may deduce that $u^2 \in N$, which is precisely what we wished to show. We are reduced then to the case where $(x, y) = 0$, $(x, z) = 0$, and $(y, z) = 0$. But then $(xy, z) = 3(x, y, z)$ and $(yx, z) = 3(y, x, z)$ follow as a result of (6), so that $6(x, y, z) = 0$. Again we are reduced to the case where $3 = 0$. Now by induction and (6) it becomes clear that the ring generated by x, y, and z is commutative. At this point Lemma 6 suffices to prove that $u = 0$. This completes the proof of the lemma.

4. THE CONSTRUCTION OF CAYLEY-DICKSON ALGEBRAS

For our purposes it will be desirable to define a Cayley-Dickson algebra in terms of its multiplication table. A Cayley-Dickson algebra is an eight-dimensional vector space over a field F, having basis elements $u_0, u_1, \cdots, u_7$ where u_0 acts as a unit element and the rest of the multiplication table looks as follows:

	u_1	u_2	u_3	u_4	u_5	u_6	u_7
u_1	αu_0	u_3	αu_2	u_5	αu_4	$-u_7$	$-\alpha u_6$
u_2	$-u_3$	βu_0	$-\beta u_1$	u_6	u_7	βu_4	βu_5
u_3	$-\alpha u_2$	βu_1	$-\alpha\beta u_0$	u_7	αu_6	$-\beta u_5$	$-\alpha\beta u_4$
u_4	$-u_5$	$-u_6$	$-u_7$	γu_0	$-\gamma u_1$	$-\gamma u_2$	$-\gamma u_3$
u_5	$-\alpha u_4$	$-u_7$	$-\alpha u_6$	γu_1	$-\alpha\gamma u_0$	γu_3	$\alpha\gamma u_2$
u_6	u_7	$-\beta u_4$	βu_5	γu_2	$-\gamma u_3$	$-\beta\gamma u_0$	$-\beta\gamma u_1$
u_7	αu_6	$-\beta u_5$	$\alpha\beta u_4$	γu_3	$-\alpha\gamma u_2$	$\beta\gamma u_1$	$\alpha\beta\gamma u_0$

It is assumed that α, β, γ are nonzero scalars.

It is a strenuous but straightforward exercise to verify that this algebra is in fact alternative. We leave this to the reader, with the comment that one can see from the multiplication table that $u_i u_j + u_j u_i = 0$ for $i, j > 0$ and $i \neq j$. This makes squaring elements a simple task and also makes it easy to observe that every element satisfies a quadratic polynomial equation over $F u_0 = F$.

In general a Cayley-Dickson algebra need not be a division algebra. Exact conditions on α, β, γ and the field F that will make the algebra a division algebra may be found in [26]. The Cayley numbers result when we choose F to be the real numbers and $\alpha = \beta = \gamma = -1$. Conversely, given a Cayley-Dickson division algebra over the field of real numbers, α, β, γ can be shown to be negative numbers. But then without loss of generality we can choose them to be all -1, so that we obtain the ordinary Cayley numbers. The Cayley numbers have the property that every pair of elements that do not commute generate an algebra isomorphic to the quaternions. In addition, the Cayley numbers do form a division algebra over the reals. It has been shown by Bott, Hirzebruch, Kervaire, and Milnor that the only finite-dimensional division algebras over the reals must have dimensions 1, 2, 4, or 8, so that the Cayley numbers again are found to be linked in a very special way to the reals, complexes, and quaternions [23].

The proof of the main theorem will now be accomplished in two steps.

THEOREM 1: *If $R \neq N$, then R contains a subring isomorphic to a Cayley-Dickson algebra.*

Proof: In Sec. 3 we noted that R had to have a unit element. Denote it by u_0. Because of Lemma 6 R cannot be commutative. Let x, y be arbitrary elements of R with the property that $v = (x, y) \neq 0$. Now Lemma 5 can be brought into play to show that there exists an element z in R such that $u = (x, y, z) \neq 0$. Lemma 3 enters and we see that $uv + vu = 0$. Hence $uv - vu \neq 0$. Consequently, bringing in Lemma 5 once more, there must exist some element t in R such that $w = (u, v, t) \neq 0$. Then we define $u_1 = u$, $u_2 = v$, $u_3 = uv$, $u_4 = w$, $u_5 = uw$, $u_6 = vw$, $u_7 = (uv)w$. Note that

$$uw = u(u, v, t) = (u, vu, t) = -(u, uv, t) = -(u, v, t)u = -wu.$$

Similarly, it may be shown that $vw = -wv$. Then the elements u, v, w satisfy the hypothesis of Lemma 7 and hence

$$\sigma(u)\sigma(v) \cdot \sigma(w) = \operatorname{sgn} \sigma(uv \cdot w) \quad \text{and} \quad \sigma(u) \cdot \sigma(v)\sigma(w)$$
$$= \operatorname{sgn} \sigma(u \cdot vw).$$

Again because of Lemma 3, $(u, v)(u, v, t) + (u, v, t)(u, v) = 0$. But $uv + vu = 0$, so that $(u, v) = 2uv$ and $(u, v, t) = w$. Hence

$$2uv \cdot w + 2w \cdot uv = 0.$$

In that case $(uv)w = -w(uv)$. But $-w(uv) = -u(vw)$, since we are using an even permutation σ, and so $(uv)w = -u(vw)$. Then we may summarize by stating that

$$\sigma(u)\sigma(v) \cdot \sigma(w) = -\sigma(u) \cdot \sigma(v)\sigma(w) = \operatorname{sgn} \sigma(uv \cdot w).$$

As a result of Lemmas 4, 8, and 9, we have u^2, v^2, and $w^2 \in C$. By letting $u^2 = \alpha$, $v^2 = \beta$, and $w^2 = \gamma$, we have enough information to determine the entire multiplication table of the u_j. We leave the general task of verification to the reader but offer the following sample calculation as a guide: $u_7 u_5 = (uv \cdot w)(uw)$. However, $(uv \cdot w) = v \cdot uw$ and so

$$(uv \cdot w)(uw) = (v \cdot uw)(uw) = v(uw)^2,$$

because of the alternative identity. But $(uw)^2 = -u^2w^2 = -\alpha\gamma u_0$. Thus

$$v(uw)^2 = -\alpha\gamma v = -\alpha\gamma u_2.$$

If we can only show that $u_0, u_1, \cdots, u_7$ are linearly independent vectors over C, then the subring generated by these vectors will indeed be isomorphic to a Cayley-Dickson algebra. Suppose then that

$$s = \delta_0 u_0 + \delta_1 u_1 + \cdots + \delta_7 u_7 = 0,$$

where $\delta_j \in C$. Forming $0 = u_i s + s u_i = 2u_i(\delta_0 u_0 + \delta_i u_i)$ implies that $\delta_0 u_0 + \delta_i u_i = 0$. Since $\delta_0 u_0 \in C$ and $u_i \notin C$ for $i > 0$, we conclude that $\delta_i = 0$ when $i > 0$. But then $\delta_0 u_0 = 0$, so that $\delta_0 = 0$. The vectors $u_0, u_1, \cdots, u_7$ are then linearly independent over C, thus completing the proof of the theorem.

It seems remarkable that the general construction employed in Theorem 1 should always lead to a Cayley-Dickson algebra, even though one doesn't know yet that R itself is a Cayley-Dickson algebra. Suddenly all the previous lemmas are seen in their proper settings and the earlier computations seem justified. The end is now nearly in sight as we prove

THEOREM 2: *If* $R \neq N$, *then* R *is a Cayley-Dickson division algebra.*

Proof: Let D be the Cayley-Dickson algebra over C that is contained in R as a result of Theorem 1. It remains to be shown that $D = R$. Let us suppose that $D \neq R$. Then there exists an element p that is contained in R but not in D. Since $C \subset D$, $p \notin C$ and consequently there exist elements $q, r \in R$ such that $u = (p, q, r) \neq 0$. We shall prove that every such p satisfies a monic, quadratic polynomial equation over C. First it can be noted that

$$u^2p^2 - (upu + u^2p)p + (up)^2 = 0.$$

Since $up = (p, q, r)p = (p, pq, r)$, it follows that $(up)^2 = (p, pq, r)^2 \in C$, making use of Lemmas 9 and 4. For the same reasons $u^2 \in C$, and also

$$(p, pq + q, r)^2 - (p, q, r)^2 - (p, pq, r)^2 = (p, pq, r)(p, q, r)$$
$$+ (p, q, r)(p, pq, r) = upu + u^2p \in C.$$

Then p does satisfy a quadratic polynomial equation over C. Multiplying through by p^{-2} makes it monic. If $p^2 - \rho p + \tau = 0$, where $\rho, \tau \in C$, then $(p - \rho/2)^2 \in C$. Thus, without loss of generality, we could have selected $p \notin D$ such that $p^2 \in C$. Let $u_0, u_1, \cdots, u_7$ be the basis of D described in the multiplication table. Then $p + u_i$ and $p - u_i$ are not in D. Hence they too satisfy monic, quadratic polynomial equations over C. Suppose that $(p + u_i)^2 = c_1(p + u_i) + c_2$ and $(p - u_i)^2 = c_3(p - u_i) + c_4$, with $c_j \in C$. Adding the two equations, we get

$$(c_1 + c_3)p + (c_1 - c_3)u_i + c_5 = 0,$$

where $c_5 = c_2 + c_4 - 2p^2 - 2u_i^2 \in C$. Since $p \notin D$, we conclude that $c_1 + c_3 = 0$. But then since $u_i \notin C$, it must also be true that $c_1 - c_3 = 0$. Consequently, $c_1 = c_3 = 0$ and $(p + u_i)^2 = c_2$. Then clearly

$$pu_i + u_ip = c_2 - p^2 - u_i^2 \in C.$$

Let us set $pu_i + u_ip = d_i \in C$. Choose

$$m = p - (d_1/2u_1^2)u_1 - \cdots - (d_7/2u_7^2)u_7.$$

Then
$$mu_j + u_jm = pu_j + u_jp - d_j = 0.$$

Also we note from the way we defined m that $m \notin D$. The triple m, u_1, u_4 are pairwise anticommutative and therefore Lemma 7 applies. Consequently,

$$u_1(mu_4) = m(u_4u_1) = -mu_5 = u_5m = -(u_4u_1)m = -(mu_4)u_1.$$

Similarly, $u_2(mu_4) = -(mu_4)u_2$. Therefore Lemma 7 applies to the triple $u_1, u_2,$ and mu_4 of pairwise anticommutative elements as well. At this point a contradiction results because there are simply too many anticommutative elements. If we use Lemma 7 repeatedly,

$$mu_7 = -u_7m = -(u_3u_4)m = (mu_4)u_3 = (mu_4)(u_1u_2)$$
$$= -u_1[(mu_4)u_2] = u_1[(u_2u_4)m] = u_1(u_6m)$$
$$= m(u_1u_6) = -mu_7.$$

But then $2mu_7 = 0$. Since $2u_7 \neq 0$, $m = 0$, which contradicts $m \notin D$. This contradiction arose out of the assumption that $R \neq$

D. Therefore $R = D$, so that R is a Cayley-Dickson algebra. Since R is a division ring this Cayley-Dickson algebra must in fact be a Cayley-Dickson division algebra. This completes the proof of the theorem.

MAIN THEOREM: *An alternative division ring in which* $1 + 1 \neq 0$ *is either an associative division ring or else isomorphic to an eight-dimensional Cayley-Dickson division algebra over its center.*

Proof: This is merely a restatement of Theorem 2.

Associative division rings, whether finite-dimensional or not, are relatively abundant. In fact, if anything, the finite-dimensional ones are rarer. Our main theorem presents an interesting contrast, for there simply do not exist infinite-dimensional alternative division rings over their center other than associative ones. This serves to substantiate once more the distinguished role of the Cayley numbers.

5. SUGGESTIONS FOR FURTHER READING

The bibliography includes a few of the many publications connected with the subject of alternative rings and its applications; some of these deserve special mention. The classification of alternative division rings is due to Bruck, the author, and Skornyakov [5, 16, and 28]. For an introduction to some of the geometrical aspects of alternative division rings, there is an excellent paper by Bruck [4]. The projective planes coordinatized by alternative division rings turn out to be an important class geometrically and the classification of alternative division rings turns out to have important applications. Some of the number theoretic aspects of alternative rings are discussed in a paper by Kaplansky [15]. Integral Cayley numbers are treated by Coxeter [7]. More general results about the structure of simple alternative rings are due to Albert and the author [2, 17, and 20]. Alternative rings are also closely connected to Jordan rings. For an introductory article on nonassociative algebras, the reader is referred to a paper by Schafer [27].

BIBLIOGRAPHY

1. Albert, A. A., "Absolute-valued algebraic algebras," *Bulletin of the American Mathematical Society*, Vol. 55 (1949), pp. 763–768.

2. Albert, A. A., "On simple alternative rings," *Canadian Journal of Mathematics*, Vol. 4 (1952), pp. 129–135.

3. van der Blij, F., "History of the octaves," *Nederlands Tijdschrift voor Natuurkunde*, Vol. 34 (1961), pp. 106–125.

4. Bruck, R. H., "Recent advances in the foundations of Euclidean plane geometry," Slaught Memorial Paper No. 4, *American Mathematical Monthly*, Vol. 62 (1955), pp. 2–17.

5. Bruck, R. H., and E. Kleinfeld, "The structure of alternative division rings," *Proceedings of the American Mathematical Society*, Vol. 2 (1951), pp. 878–890.

6. Cayley, A., "On Jacobi's elliptic functions, in reply to Rev. Brice Brownin and on quaternions," *Philosophical Magazine and Journal of Science*, Vol. 3 (1845), pp. 210–213.

7. Coxeter, H. S. M., "Integral Cayley numbers," *Duke Mathematical Journal*, Vol. 13 (1946), pp. 561–578.

8. Dickson, L. E., "On quaternions and their generalizations and the history of the eight square theorem," *Annals of Mathematics*, Vol. 20 (1919), pp. 155–171.

9. Freudenthal, H., "Zur ebenen Oktavengeometrie," *Proceedings of the Koninklijke Nederlandse Akademie van Wetenschappen, Series A*, Vol. 56 (1953), pp. 195–200.

10. Hall, M., "Projective planes," *Transactions of the American Mathematical Society*, Vol. 54 (1943), pp. 229–277.

11. Hamilton, W. R., "Note respecting the research of J. T. Graves," *Transactions of the Royal Irish Academy*, Vol. 21 (1848), pp. 338–341.

12. Hurwitz, A., Über die Composition der quadratischen Formen von beliebig vielen Variabeln," *Nachrichten von der königlichen Gesellschaft der Wissenschaften in Göttingen* (1898), pp. 309–316.

13. Jacobson, N., "Structure of alternative and Jordan bimodules," *Osaka Mathematical Journal*, Vol. 6 (1954), pp. 1–71.

14. Kaplansky, I., "Semi-simple alternative rings," *Portugaliae Mathematica*, Vol. 10 (1951), pp. 37–50.

15. Kaplansky, I., "Infinite-dimensional quadratic forms admitting composition," *Proceedings of the American Mathematical Society*, Vol. 4 (1953), pp. 956–960.

16. Kleinfeld, E., "Alternative division rings of characteristic 2," *Proceedings of the National Academy of Science of the United States of America*, Vol. 37 (1951), pp. 818–820.

17. Kleinfeld, E., "Simple alternative rings," *Annals of Mathematics*, Vol. 58 (1953), pp. 544–547.

18. Kleinfeld, E., "Primitive alternative rings and semi-simplicity," *American Journal of Mathematics*, Vol. 77 (1955), pp. 725–730.

19. Kleinfeld, E., "Generalization of a theorem on simple alternative rings," *Portugaliae Mathematica*, Vol. 14 (1955), pp. 91–94.

20. Kleinfeld, E., "Alternative nil rings," *Annals of Mathematics*, Vol. 66 (1957), pp. 395–399.

21. Kleinfeld, E., "On alternative and right alternative rings," National Academy of Science-National Research Council Publication 502 (1957), pp. 20–23.

22. Mahler, K., "On ideals in the Cayley-Dickson algebra," *Proceedings of the Royal Irish Academy*, Vol. 48 (1943), pp. 123–133.

23. Milnor, J., "Some consequences of a theorem of Bott," *Annals of Mathematics*, Vol. 68 (1958), pp. 444–449.

24. Moufang, R., "Alternativkörper und der Satz vom vollständigen Vierseit (D_9)," *Abhandlungen aus dem Mathematischen Seminar, Hamburg*, Vol. 9 (1933), pp. 207–222.

25. Pickert, G., *Projektive Ebenen*. Berlin: Springer-Verlag, 1955.

26. Schafer, R. D., "Alternative algebras over an arbitrary field," *Bulletin of the American Mathematical Society*, Vol. 49 (1943), pp. 549–555.

27. Schafer, R. D., "Structure and representation of nonassociative algebras," *Bulletin of the American Mathematical Society*, Vol. 61 (1955), pp. 469–484.

28. Skornyakov, L. A., "Alternative fields," *Ukrainskii Matematicheskii Žurnal*, Vol. 2 (1950), pp. 70–85 (Russian).

29. Smiley, M. F., "The radical of an alternative ring," *Annals of Mathematics*, Vol. 49 (1948), pp. 702–709.

30. Smiley, M. F., "Some questions concerning alternative rings," *Bulletin of the American Mathematical Society*, Vol. 57 (1951), pp. 36–43.

31. Springer, T. A., "The projective octave plane I, II," *Proceedings of the Koninklijke Nederlandse Akademie van Wetenschappen, Series A*, Vol. 63 (1960), pp. 74–101.

32. Zorn, M., "Theorie der alternativen Ringe," *Abhandlungen aus dem Mathematischen Seminar, Hamburg*, Vol. 8 (1930), pp. 123–147.

JORDAN ALGEBRAS

Lowell J. Paige

1. INTRODUCTION

Our primary aim in this paper is to give the general development of a theory for Jordan algebras and to relate that theory to other classes of algebras. For this purpose, it will be necessary to be more general in the first few sections than the title might indicate.

A *nonassociative algebra* $\mathfrak{A}$ is initially a vector space over a field Φ for which a multiplication of vectors is prescribed. The scalar multiplication and addition in $\mathfrak{A}$, as a vector space, are related to the multiplication of elements, indicated simply by juxtaposition xy, by imposing the following properties:

(1) $\qquad (\alpha a)(\beta b) = (\alpha\beta)(ab) \qquad$ for all $\alpha, \beta \in \Phi$, $a, b \in \mathfrak{A}$.

(2) Distributive laws $\qquad \begin{cases} a(b + c) = ab + ac \\ (b + c)a = ba + ca \end{cases} \qquad$ for all $a, b, c \in \mathfrak{A}$.

If, in addition to (1) and (2), the multiplication of elements is associative,

(3) $(ab)c = a(bc)$ for all a, b, $c \in \mathfrak{A}$,

then $\mathfrak{A}$ is an associative algebra over the field Φ.

Quite frequently in present-day mathematics, one replaces the field Φ occurring in the definition of a vector space by a commutative ring with unity. This generalization may be carried over to algebras, in which case we would begin with a Φ-module rather than a vector space. One advantage of this procedure is that ring analogues of various classes of algebras may be studied simultaneously with the algebras. However, we feel that the development of a theory for algebras, as defined above, will be sufficient for our purposes. The general agreement in mathematical literature is that the term *algebra*, without any modifier, denotes an associative algebra. We shall often use the term in this paper in the more general sense of nonassociative algebra, and when associativity is to be assumed it will normally be stated explicitly.

A simple example of a *not*-associative algebra is obtained when one verifies that the cross (or vector) product of vectors in euclidean space is a multiplication of vectors satisfying (1) and (2). Here, we have additionally the identities

$$\vec{X} \times \vec{X} = 0, \qquad \vec{X} \times \vec{Y} = -\vec{Y} \times \vec{X},$$
$$(\vec{X} \times \vec{Y}) \times \vec{Z} = \vec{X} \times (\vec{Y} \times \vec{Z}) + \vec{Y} \times (\vec{Z} \times \vec{X}).$$

In the last equation, it is a simple matter to find vectors $\vec{X}$, $\vec{Y}$, and $\vec{Z}$ such that $\vec{Y} \times (\vec{Z} \times \vec{X}) \neq 0$, and consequently we do not have an associative algebra. The usefulness of this nonassociative algebra needs no illustration. It is to be noted that the similar interpretation for the scalar (or dot) product of vectors will not yield an algebra except in the case that $\mathfrak{A} = \Phi$.

The imposition of additional identities satisfied by the elements of a nonassociative algebra, such as those for $\vec{X} \times \vec{Y}$, is typical. The facts of the matter are that nonassociative algebras, without additional identities, simply have a meager theory and even fewer applications.

The natural generalization of the preceding example to a nonassociative algebra satisfying

(4) $a^2 = 0$ (or $ab = -ba$)   for all $a, b \in \mathfrak{A}$,

and the *Jacobi identity*

(5) $(ab)c + (bc)a + (ca)b = 0$ for all $a, b, c \in \mathfrak{A}$,

is called a *Lie algebra*. The general theory of Lie algebras has been developed extensively and many applications of the theory are to be found in other branches of mathematics. An account of this theory may be found in [15].

The class of algebras we wish to discuss are those nonassociative algebras $\mathfrak{A}$ over a field Φ that satisfy the identities

(6) $ab = ba$,

(7) $a^2(ba) = (a^2b)a$

for all $a, b \in \mathfrak{A}$. The initial study of these algebras occurs in a 1933 paper by Professor P. Jordan entitled "Über Verallgemeinerungmöglichkeiten des Formalismus der Quantenmechanik." It requires no knowledge of German to gather that we are dealing with a class of algebras that had its origin outside the field of algebra. The name *Jordan algebras* was introduced by A. A. Albert in a paper [1] that extended earlier results for the case that the algebra was formally real (that is, $\Sigma_1^n x_i^2 = 0$ if and only if all $x_i = 0$ [13] to Jordan algebras over an arbitrary field. On a recent visit to the United States, Professor Jordan was surprised to learn that his original systems of r-numbers are now known formally as *Jordan algebras*.

An attempt has been made to keep this paper as elementary as possible. Nonetheless, we have had to make assumptions about the mathematical preparation of our readers. The assumptions have been kept to a minimum and are mentioned in Sec. 2 together with the terminology and notation to be used throughout the paper.

Sections 3 and 4 are devoted to examples of Jordan algebras obtainable from associative algebras, a relationship between Lie and Jordan algebras, and an application to Jordan homomorphisms. In Sec. 5 we turn our attention to abstract Jordan algebras.

Simple consequences of the identities defining a Jordan algebra are determined for future reference.

A brief account of the structure theorems for finite-dimensional associative algebras is outlined in Sec. 6 as a basis for comparison with the structure theorems we obtain for Jordan algebras in Secs. 7 and 8. In each of these sections we have found it convenient to permit some generality and we often discuss arbitrary nonassociative algebras. The structure theorems for simple Jordan algebras are postponed until Sec. 10 in order to permit a discussion in Sec. 9 of idempotents and the Pierce decomposition necessary for our classification.

In the classification of simple Jordan algebras, we find one particular class that behaves in an exceptional manner. These "exceptional" Jordan algebras are discussed in some detail in Sec. 11, and unsolved problems are indicated. Finally, in Sec. 12 we try to make amends for omitting many interesting aspects of Jordan algebras. We can only direct the readers' attention to interesting areas still demanding research and investigation.

A few cautionary remarks are in order. We have assumed throughout that we are dealing with finite-dimensional algebras over a field Φ even though many of our definitions are quite appropriate to the more general case. The fields Φ are always assumed to be of characteristic $\neq 2$ when discussing Jordan algebras. We add further restrictions on the characteristic in later sections and, although practically all of the theorems are valid for arbitrary characteristic $\neq 2$, we assume beyond Sec. 8 that the fields Φ are of characteristic 0.

No attempt will be made to give a complete bibliography of papers devoted to the development of the theory and applications of Jordan algebras. Occasionally, we shall make reference to a specific paper because the subject matter is especially appropriate to the discussion; but, in general, we direct the readers' attention to the papers by Professor R. D. Schafer [19, 20] for a complete bibliography. We take this opportunity to point out that the many papers of Professors Albert, Cohn, Jacobson, and Schafer have guided our discussion. Moreover, Professor Jacobson has

made available to us notes on Jordan algebras that will appear
in a forthcoming book on the subject.

2. TERMINOLOGY AND NOTATION

We shall assume a knowledge of the definitions and elementary
results from the theory of vector spaces. In particular, if $\mathfrak{A}$ and $\mathfrak{B}$
are vector spaces over Φ, a mapping T of $\mathfrak{A}$ into $\mathfrak{B}$ such that

$$(8) \qquad (x + y)T = xT + yT, \qquad (\alpha x)T = \alpha(xT)$$

for all $x, y \in \mathfrak{A}$, $\alpha \in \Phi$ will be called a *linear transformation* (linear
mapping) of $\mathfrak{A}$ into $\mathfrak{B}$. A knowledge of the theory for linear transformations, their representation as matrices for finite-dimensional
vector spaces, and the definitions from the theory of associative
algebras will also be presupposed.

The concepts in the theory of associative algebras that do not
depend upon the associative law of multiplication in their formulation have unambiguous analogues in the theory of nonassociative
algebras. For example, if $\mathfrak{A}$ and $\mathfrak{B}$ are nonassociative algebras over
a field Φ, a linear mapping T of $\mathfrak{A}$ into $\mathfrak{B}$ (as vector spaces over Φ)
such that

$$(9) \qquad (xy)T = xTyT \qquad \text{for all } x, y \in \mathfrak{A}$$

is a *homomorphism* of $\mathfrak{A}$ into $\mathfrak{B}$. Similarly, we have the concept of
an *isomorphism* (T is a biunique mapping of $\mathfrak{A}$ onto $\mathfrak{B}$), an *endo-
morphism* (T is a homomorphism of $\mathfrak{A}$ into $\mathfrak{A}$), and an *automorphism*
(T is an isomorphism of $\mathfrak{A}$ onto $\mathfrak{A}$).

If $\mathfrak{H}$ and $\mathfrak{K}$ are subsets of a nonassociative algebra $\mathfrak{A}$, we denote
by $\mathfrak{H}\mathfrak{K}$ the subspace of $\mathfrak{A}$ spanned by all products hk for $h \in \mathfrak{H}$,
$k \in \mathfrak{K}$. A subspace $\mathfrak{H}$ of $\mathfrak{A}$ is called a *subalgebra* if $\mathfrak{H}\mathfrak{H} \subseteq \mathfrak{H}$, a
right ideal if $\mathfrak{H}\mathfrak{A} \subseteq \mathfrak{H}$, a *left ideal* if $\mathfrak{A}\mathfrak{H} \subseteq \mathfrak{H}$, and simply an *ideal*
if $\mathfrak{H}$ is both a right and left ideal of $\mathfrak{A}$.

The kernel $\mathfrak{K}$ of a homomorphism T of a nonassociative algebra
$\mathfrak{A}$ into a nonassociative algebra $\mathfrak{B}$ consists of all elements $a \in \mathfrak{A}$
such that $aT = 0$ and $\mathfrak{K}$ is an ideal in $\mathfrak{A}$. As in the associative
theory, the quotient algebra $\mathfrak{A}/\mathfrak{K}$ is obtained by considering the

vector space cosets $(a + \Re)$ as elements of an algebra for which we define

$$(a + \Re) + (b + \Re) = (a + b) + \Re,$$
$$\alpha(a + \Re) = \alpha a + \Re,$$
$$(a + \Re)(b + \Re) = ab + \Re$$

for all a, $b \in \mathfrak{A}$, $\alpha \in \Phi$. The mapping $(a + \Re) \longrightarrow aT$ is an isomorphism of the quotient algebra $\mathfrak{A}/\Re$ onto the subalgebra $\mathfrak{A}T \subseteq \mathfrak{B}$. Of course, a quotient algebra $\mathfrak{A}/\Re$ can be constructed for any ideal $\Re \subseteq \mathfrak{A}$ and $\mathfrak{A}/\Re$ will be a homomorphic image of $\mathfrak{A}$ under the mapping $a \longrightarrow a + \Re$.

It is possible for $\mathfrak{A}$ to be a nonassociative algebra and a quotient algebra $\mathfrak{A}/\Re$ to be associative. On the other hand, if we have an identity for $\mathfrak{A}$ such as

$$(a^2b)a = a^2(ba),$$

then

$$\{(a + \Re)^2(b + \Re)\}(a + \Re) = (a^2b)a + \Re = a^2(ba) + \Re$$
$$= (a + \Re)^2\{(b + \Re)(a + \Re)\},$$

so that the same identity is valid in any homomorphic image of $\mathfrak{A}$. A similar argument for the commutativity of a Jordan algebra is valid, and we see that any homomorphic image of a Jordan algebra is again a Jordan algebra. The homomorphic images of Lie algebras are again Lie algebras, and in general a class of algebras defined by a set of identities will be closed under the operation of taking homomorphic images.

If $\mathfrak{A}$ and $\mathfrak{B}$ are nonassociative algebras over a field Φ, the direct sum $\mathfrak{A} \oplus \mathfrak{B}$ of $\mathfrak{A}$ and $\mathfrak{B}$ as vector spaces can be made into an algebra by defining a product

$$(a_1, b_1)(a_2, b_2) = (a_1a_2, b_1b_2)$$

for elements (a_1, b_1), $(a_2, b_2) \in \mathfrak{A} \oplus \mathfrak{B}$. Note that $\mathfrak{A} \oplus \mathfrak{B}$ contains ideals $\{(a, 0)|a \in \mathfrak{A}\}$ and $\{(0, b)|b \in \mathfrak{B}\}$ isomorphic to $\mathfrak{A}$ and $\mathfrak{B}$, and these ideals may be denoted by $\mathfrak{A}$ and $\mathfrak{B}$ without confusion. It should be clear that $\mathfrak{A} \oplus \mathfrak{B}$ is a Jordan algebra if $\mathfrak{A}$ and $\mathfrak{B}$ are Jordan algebras.

The preceding definition can be extended to the direct sum of any finite number of algebras $\mathfrak{A}_i$ in a rather obvious manner, and such a direct sum of Jordan algebras is again a Jordan algebra. In fact, the complete direct sum of an indexed set of Jordan algebras is again a Jordan algebra.

The importance of considering subalegbras, homomorphic images, and direct sums of algebras lies in the fact that a class of algebras defined by a set of identities (for example, those for Jordan algebras, Lie algebras, alternative algebras) is closed with respect to these operations. Conversely, a special case of a result of Garrett Birkhoff [9] implies that any class of nonassociative algebras that is closed under the operations of taking subalgebras, homomorphic images, and complete direct sums can be defined by a set of identities. Unsolved problems in this direction for Jordan algebras will be indicated in Secs. 3 and 12.

3. JORDAN AND LIE ALGEBRAS DERIVED FROM ASSOCIATIVE ALGEBRAS

Let $\mathfrak{A}$ be an associative algebra over a field Φ of characteristic not two. In terms of the associative multiplication of elements in $\mathfrak{A}$, written $a \cdot b$, define new operations

$$(10) \qquad [a, b] = a \cdot b - b \cdot a,$$

$$(11) \qquad ab = \tfrac{1}{2}(a \cdot b + b \cdot a).$$

We note that

$$[\alpha a, \beta b] = \alpha a \cdot \beta b - \beta b \cdot \alpha a = (\alpha\beta)(a \cdot b - b \cdot a) = (\alpha\beta)[a, b],$$

$$(\alpha a)(\beta b) = \tfrac{1}{2}(\alpha a \cdot \beta b + \beta b \cdot \alpha a) = (\alpha\beta)\tfrac{1}{2}(a \cdot b + b \cdot a) = (\alpha\beta)ab$$

for all $a, b \in \mathfrak{A}$, $\alpha, \beta \in \Phi$. Thus the new multiplications $[a, b]$ and ab satisfy property (1) imposed upon a product in a nonassociative algebra. Similarly, it is a simple matter to verify that the distributive laws of (2) are satisfied for $[a, b]$ and ab. If we retain the vector space structure of $\mathfrak{A}$ and replace the associative multiplication by $[a, b]$ or ab, we obtain new algebras over Φ which we shall denote by $\mathfrak{A}^-$ and $\mathfrak{A}^+$, respectively.

The multiplication $[a, b]$ of $\mathfrak{A}^-$ is called the *commutator* of elements in $\mathfrak{A}$. Several identities for this multiplication are easily established. We see that

(12) $$[a, a] = a \cdot a - a \cdot a = 0,$$

(13) $$[a, b] = a \cdot b - b \cdot a = -[b, a].$$

The identity (12) states that the square of every element in $\mathfrak{A}^-$ is zero and if a is replaced by $x + y$, we obtain

$$0 = [x + y, x + y] = [x, x + y] + [y, x + y]$$
$$= [x, x] + [x, y] + [y, x] + [y, y] = [x, y] + [y, x].$$

Thus the identity (13) is implied by (12), and conversely, if we replace b by a in the antisymmetric relation (13), it follows that $2[a, a] = 0$ or $[a, a] = 0$, since Φ is a field of characteristic not two.

The process used to obtain (13) as a consequence of (12) is called the *linearization of an identity;* an identity that is not linear in an element is replaced by an equivalent identity that is linear in each element that appears. We shall have occasion to use this process again since it is a common technique in the theory of nonassociative algebras.

If the multiplication $[a, b]$ were associative, we would have $[[a, b], c] = [a, [b, c]]$; however,

$$[[a, b], c] = a \cdot b \cdot c + c \cdot b \cdot a - b \cdot a \cdot c - c \cdot a \cdot b,$$
$$[a, [b, c]] = a \cdot b \cdot c + c \cdot b \cdot a - b \cdot c \cdot a - a \cdot c \cdot b.$$

Therefore the multiplication $[a, b]$ is not necessarily associative. It is a straightforward verification that the multiplication $[a, b]$ satisfies the Jacobi identity

$$[[a, b], c] + [[b, c], a] + [[c, a], b] = 0.$$

Hence $\mathfrak{A}^-$ is a Lie algebra.

In the introduction, Lie algebras were defined to be those non-associative algebras satisfying the identities

$$a^2 = 0, \qquad (ab)c + (bc)a + (ca)b = 0.$$

One of the fundamental results in the theory of Lie algebras is the

Poincaré-Birkhoff-Witt theorem that states that every Lie algebra is isomorphic to a subalgebra of some algebra $\mathfrak{A}^-$.

Let us now turn to the algebra $\mathfrak{A}^+$ and its Jordan product

$$ab = \tfrac{1}{2}(a\cdot b + b\cdot a).$$

We note first that this multiplication is commutative and that powers of an element a are the same for either the associative product $a\cdot b$ or the product ab. Furthermore,

$$
\begin{aligned}
4a^2(ba) &= a^2\cdot(b\cdot a + a\cdot b) + (b\cdot a + a\cdot b)\cdot a^2 \\
&= a^2\cdot b\cdot a + a^3\cdot b + b\cdot a^3 + a\cdot b\cdot a^2,
\end{aligned}
$$

$$
\begin{aligned}
4(a^2b)a &= (a^2\cdot b + b\cdot a^2)\cdot a + a\cdot(a^2\cdot b + b\cdot a^2) \\
&= a^2\cdot b\cdot a + b\cdot a^3 + a^3\cdot b + a\cdot b\cdot a^2,
\end{aligned}
$$

so that the elements of $\mathfrak{A}^+$ satisfy the identities

$$ab = ba,$$
$$a^2(ba) = (a^2b)a.$$

Hence $\mathfrak{A}^+$ is a Jordan algebra.

The analogue of the Poincaré-Birkhoff-Witt theorem for Lie algebras is not valid for Jordan algebras. We shall see that there are Jordan algebras that are *not* isomorphic to a subalgebra of any Jordan algebra $\mathfrak{A}^+$. If a Jordan algebra $\mathfrak{J}$ is isomorphic to a subalgebra of $\mathfrak{A}^+$ ($\mathfrak{A}$ associatvie), then $\mathfrak{J}$ is called a *special* Jordan algebra. The Jordan algebras that are not special are called *exceptional* Jordan algebras.

Special Jordan algebras have been characterized by P. J. Cohn [10], and we shall give one version here that illustrates a relation among the products $[a,\,b]$, ab, and $a\cdot b$ of an associative algebra $\mathfrak{A}$. Between the products $[a,\,b]$ of $\mathfrak{A}^-$ and ab of $\mathfrak{A}^+$, we have the identity

$$(14) \quad [a,\,b^2] = a\cdot b^2 - b^2\cdot a$$
$$= (a\cdot b - b\cdot a)\cdot b + b\cdot(a\cdot b - b\cdot a) = 2[a,\,b]b.$$

Furthermore, since

$$
\begin{aligned}
[a,\,[b,\,c]] &= a\cdot[b,\,c] - [b,\,c]\cdot a = a\cdot(b\cdot c - c\cdot b) - (b\cdot c - c\cdot b)\cdot a \\
&= a\cdot b\cdot c - a\cdot c\cdot b - b\cdot c\cdot a + c\cdot b\cdot a,
\end{aligned}
$$

as well as

$$4\{(ab)c - (ac)b\} = 4\left\{\frac{a \cdot b + b \cdot a}{2} \cdot \frac{c}{2} + \frac{c}{2} \cdot \frac{a \cdot b + b \cdot a}{2}\right\}$$

$$- 4\left\{\frac{a \cdot c + c \cdot a}{2} \cdot \frac{b}{2} + \frac{b}{2} \cdot \frac{a \cdot c + c \cdot a}{2}\right\}$$

$$= a \cdot b \cdot c + c \cdot b \cdot a - a \cdot c \cdot b - b \cdot c \cdot a,$$

we have the identity

(15) $$[a, [b, c]] = 4\{(ab)c - (ac)b\}.$$

By replacing c by b^2 in (15), we see that (15) and (14) imply

$$4\{(ab)b^2 - (ab^2)b\} = [a, [b, b^2]] = [a, [b, b]b] = [a, 0] = 0$$

or $$(ab)b^2 = (ab^2)b.$$

Let us define a *J-algebra* to be a commutative algebra $\Re$ (with product denoted by ab) having an additional binary operation $[a, b]$ defined on $\Re$ which is bilinear, antisymmetric, and satisfies

(16) $$[a, b^2] = 2[a, b]b,$$

(17) $$[a, [b, c]] = 4\{(ab)c - (ac)b\}.$$

The preceding discussion indicates that the Jordan algebra $\mathfrak{A}^+$ ($\mathfrak{A}$ associative) may be thought of as a *J*-algebra.

Conversely, we may begin with an arbitrary *J*-algebra $\Re$ and define a new "dot" multiplication

$$a \cdot b = ab + \tfrac{1}{2}[a, b]$$

in terms of the operations already available in $\Re$. We then have

$$a \cdot a = a^2 + \tfrac{1}{2}[a, a] = a^2,$$
$$a \cdot b - b \cdot a = ab + \tfrac{1}{2}[a, b] - ba - \tfrac{1}{2}[b, a] = [a, b],$$

so that the operations ab and $[a, b]$ can be expressed by dot multiplication. The dot multiplication is associative but we shall need the linearized form of (16) in order to prove this fact. Thus, replace b by $x + y$ in (16) to obtain (after appropriate cancellations)

(18) $[a, xy] = [a, x]y + [a, y]x.$

We now compute

$$(a \cdot b) \cdot c = \{ab + \tfrac{1}{2}[a, b]\} \cdot c = \{ab + \tfrac{1}{2}[a, b]\}c + \tfrac{1}{2}[ab + \tfrac{1}{2}[a, b], c]$$
$$= (ab)c + \tfrac{1}{2}[a, b]c + \tfrac{1}{2}[ab, c] + \tfrac{1}{4}[[a, b], c]$$
$$= (ab)c + \tfrac{1}{2}[a, b]c + \tfrac{1}{2}[b, c]a + \tfrac{1}{2}[a, c]b + (cb)a - (ca)b,$$

where we have used (18) to expand $[ab, c]$ and (17) to expand $[[a, b], c]$.

A regrouping of terms on the right side of the preceding equation yields

$$(a \cdot b) \cdot c = \tfrac{1}{2}[a, b]c + \tfrac{1}{2}[a, c]b + a(bc) + \tfrac{1}{2}a[b, c] + (ab)c - (ac)b$$
$$= \tfrac{1}{2}[a, bc] + a(bc) + \tfrac{1}{2}a[b, c] + \tfrac{1}{4}[a, [b, c]]$$
$$= a \cdot (bc) + a \cdot (\tfrac{1}{2}[b, c])$$
$$= a \cdot (b \cdot c).$$

The vector space structure of $\mathfrak{R}$, together with the dot multiplication, yields an associative algebra which we denote by $\mathfrak{A}$, and we have $\mathfrak{A}^+ \cong \mathfrak{R}$. Thus, we have the result

THEOREM 3.1: *Every J-algebra is of the form $\mathfrak{A}^+$, for a suitable associative algebra $\mathfrak{A}$.*

In view of the preceding theorem, it is possible to give an equivalent definition of a special Jordan algebra: *A Jordan algebra is a special Jordan algebra if and only if it is isomorphic to a subalgebra of a J-algebra.*

The problem of determining a set of identities that distinguish the special Jordan algebras is still unsolved. It is conceivable that the preceding characterization (and another slightly more complicated alternative given by Cohn [10]) could lead to a solution of this problem.

4. FURTHER EXAMPLES OF JORDAN ALGEBRAS

We shall indicate a few more examples of Jordan algebras that will be referred to later.

1. *Jordan algebras of symmetric bilinear forms.* Let $\mathfrak{B}$ be a vector space over a field Φ and let (x, y) be a symmetric, bilinear form defined on $\mathfrak{B}$; that is, $(x, y) \in \Phi$ and

$$(a + b, c) = (a, c) + (b, c), \qquad (a, b + c) = (a, b) + (a, c),$$
$$\alpha(a, b) = (\alpha a, b) = (a, \alpha b), \qquad (a, b) = (b, a).$$

Denote by $\mathfrak{A}$ the direct sum of $\mathfrak{B}$ and Φ (as a one-dimensional vector space over Φ with basis 1); $\mathfrak{A} = \Phi 1 \oplus \mathfrak{B}$. Thus every element in $\mathfrak{A}$ has the form $\alpha 1 + a$, $\alpha \in \Phi$, $a \in \mathfrak{B}$, and we define a multiplication of elements of $\mathfrak{A}$ by

$$(19) \qquad (\alpha 1 + a)(\beta 1 + b) = \{\alpha\beta + (a, b)\}1 + \alpha b + \beta a.$$

It is a straightforward verification that this multiplication satisfies (1) and (2) so that $\mathfrak{A}$ is a nonassociative algebra over Φ. The verification that $\mathfrak{A}$ is a Jordan algebra is straightforward, and it can be shown that $\mathfrak{A}$ is a special Jordan algebra; however, the latter is not so easy and will be indicated later.

2. **-symmetric elements of an associative algebra.* Let $a \longrightarrow a^*$ be a one-to-one linear mapping of an associative algebra $\mathfrak{A}$ onto itself such that

$$(a \cdot b)^* = b^* \cdot a^*.$$

The mapping $a \longrightarrow a^*$ is called an *antiautomorphism* of $\mathfrak{A}$. For the Jordan algebra $\mathfrak{A}^+$, we note that

$$(ab)^* = \tfrac{1}{2}(a \cdot b + b \cdot a)^* = \tfrac{1}{2}(b^* \cdot a^* + a^* \cdot b^*) = a^* b^*,$$

and consequently $a \longrightarrow a^*$ is an automorphism of $\mathfrak{A}^+$. The set of elements left fixed, the *-symmetric elements $a^* = a$, is a special Jordan subalgebra $\mathfrak{H}$ of $\mathfrak{A}^+$.

A simple example of the situation described above occurs when $\mathfrak{A}$ is taken to be the algebra of $n \times n$ matrices over Φ and $a \longrightarrow a^*$ is the mapping of a matrix into its transpose. The subalgebra $\mathfrak{H}$ of $\mathfrak{A}^+$ is then the set of all symmetric matrices.

3. *Symmetric elements of polynomial algebras.* Let $\Phi[x_1, x_2, \cdots, x_n]$ denote the associative algebra *but not commutative* of polyno-

mials in $x_1, x_2, \cdots, x_n$ with coefficients in Φ. Relative to the Jordan product

$$(20) \qquad xy = \tfrac{1}{2}(x \cdot y + y \cdot x),$$

we have the special Jordan algebra $\Phi[x_1, x_2, \cdots, x_n]^+$, and there are two subalgebras of importance.

First, there is the subalgebra $\mathfrak{J}_0^{(n)}$ generated by 1 and $x_1, x_2, \cdots, x_n$ with respect to the Jordan product (20); this is the subspace of $\Phi[x_1, x_2, \cdots, x_n]^+$ spanned by all possible products of the elements $1, x_1, x_2, \cdots, x_n$. The subalgebra $\mathfrak{J}_0^{(n)}$ of $\Phi[x_1, x_2, \cdots, x_n]^+$ is called the *free special Jordan algebra* on n generators and the elements of $\mathfrak{J}_0^{(n)}$ are called *Jordan polynomials* of $\Phi[x_1, x_2, \cdots, x_n]$.

An illustration of $\mathfrak{J}_0^{(n)}$ may be of value, so let us take $n = 3$ and, for convenience, $x = x_1, \ y = x_2, \ z = x_3$. Thus we begin with $\Phi[x, y, z]$ and typical monomial elements of $\mathfrak{J}_0^{(3)}$, in addition to $1, x^n, y^n, z^n \ (n = 1, 2, \cdots)$, would be

$$xy = \tfrac{1}{2}(x \cdot y + y \cdot x), \qquad xz = \tfrac{1}{2}(x \cdot z + z \cdot x),$$
$$yz = \tfrac{1}{2}(y \cdot z + z \cdot y),$$
$$(xy)y = \tfrac{1}{2}\{\tfrac{1}{2}(x \cdot y + y \cdot x) \cdot y + y \cdot \tfrac{1}{2}(x \cdot y + y \cdot x)\}$$
$$= \tfrac{1}{4}\{x \cdot y \cdot y + y \cdot y \cdot x + 2y \cdot x \cdot y\},$$
$$(x^2 z)y = \tfrac{1}{2}\{\tfrac{1}{2}(x^2 \cdot z + z \cdot x^2) \cdot y + y \cdot \tfrac{1}{2}(x^2 \cdot z + z \cdot x^2)\}$$
$$= \tfrac{1}{4}\{x^2 \cdot z \cdot y + y \cdot z \cdot x^2 + z \cdot x^2 \cdot y + y \cdot x^2 \cdot z\}.$$

We note that these elements, when expressed in terms of the associative multiplication of $\Phi[x, y, z]$ are sums of products (say $x^2 \cdot z \cdot y$) and the same elements written in reverse order ($y \cdot z \cdot x^2$). This observation leads us to describe a second subalgebra of $\Phi[x_1, x_2, \cdots, x_n]^+$.

Define a mapping * of $\Phi[x_1, x_2, \cdots, n]$ for elements of Φ and all monomials by the equations

$$\alpha^* = \alpha, \qquad (x_{i_1} \cdot x_{i_2} \cdot \cdots \cdot x_{i_k})^* = x_{i_k} \cdot \cdots \cdot x_{i_2} \cdot x_{i_1},$$

where we are not assuming that the x_i's are necessarily distinct. For example, in our illustration of $\Phi[x, y, z]$,

$$(x^2 \cdot y \cdot z^2 \cdot y^2 \cdot x)^* = x \cdot y^2 \cdot z^2 \cdot y \cdot x^2.$$

The *reversal* operator * can be extended linearly to all polynomials and the equation

$$\{(x_{i_1} \cdot x_{i_2} \cdot \; \cdots \; \cdot x_{i_k})(x_{j_1} \cdot x_{j_2} \cdot \; \cdots \; \cdot x_{j_r})\}^*$$
$$= x_{j_r} \cdot \; \cdots \; \cdot x_{j_2} \cdot x_{j_1} \cdot x_{i_k} \cdot \; \cdots \; \cdot x_{i_2} \cdot x_{i_1}$$
$$= (x_{j_1} \cdot x_{j_2} \cdot \; \cdots \; \cdot x_{j_r})^* (x_{i_1} \cdot x_{i_2} \cdot \; \cdots \; \cdot x_{i_k})^*$$

implies that the reversal operator is an antiautomorphism of period 2 (an involution) of $\Phi[x_1, x_2, \cdots, x_n]$. It follows from the discussion of Example 2 that the set $\mathfrak{H}_0^{(n)}$ of all reverse-symmetric elements ($a^* = a$) is a special Jordan subalgebra of $\Phi[x_1, x_2, \cdots, x_n]^+$.

The subalgebra $\mathfrak{H}_0^{(n)}$ contains 1, x_1, x_2, $\cdots$, x_n, and consequently we have

$$\mathfrak{H}_0^{(n)} \supseteq \mathfrak{J}_0^{(n)}.$$

The importance of the *free special Jordan algebra* lies in the fact that any special Jordan algebra $\mathfrak{A}$ (with 1) generated by 1, a_1, a_2, $\cdots$, a_n is the homomorphic image of $\mathfrak{J}_0^{(n)}$. On the other hand, Cohn [11] has shown that

$$\mathfrak{H}_0^{(2)} = \mathfrak{J}_0^{(2)}, \qquad \mathfrak{H}_0^{(3)} = \mathfrak{J}_0^{(3)}$$

and that $\mathfrak{J}_0^{(n)}$ is properly contained in $\mathfrak{H}_0^{(n)}$ for $n \geq 4$.

An application of the identification of $\mathfrak{H}_0^{(2)}$ and $\mathfrak{J}_0^{(2)}$ arises in the study of Jordan homomorphisms of an associative algebra. A *Jordan homomorphism* of an associative algebra $\mathfrak{A}$ is a linear mapping $a \longrightarrow a^*$ of $\mathfrak{A}$ into $\mathfrak{A}$ such that

(21) $(a^2)^* = (a^*)^2, \quad (a \cdot b \cdot a)^* = (a^* \cdot b^* \cdot a^*) \qquad$ for all $a, b \in \mathfrak{A}$.

Note that one side of (21) is reverse-symmetric in the elements a and b and the other side is reverse-symmetric in a^* and b^*. The identification of $\mathfrak{H}_0^{(2)}$ with $\mathfrak{J}_0^{(2)}$ implies that $a \cdot b \cdot a$ is contained in the Jordan subalgebra of $\mathfrak{A}^+$ generated by a and b while $a^* \cdot b^* \cdot a^*$ is in the Jordan subalgebra of $\mathfrak{A}^+$ generated by a^* and b^*. In particular,

(22) $a \cdot b \cdot a = (ab)a + (ba)a - (aa)b,$

(23) $a^* \cdot b^* \cdot a^* = (a^*b^*)a^* + (b^*a^*)a^* - (a^*a^*)b^*.$

Now if $a \longrightarrow a^*$ is a homomorphism of $\mathfrak{A}^+$, then it follows from (22) and (23) that $(a \cdot b \cdot a)^* = a^* \cdot b^* \cdot a^*$. Hence every homomorphism of the Jordan algebra $\mathfrak{A}^+$ is a Jordan homomorphism of $\mathfrak{A}$. On the other hand, let us assume that $a \longrightarrow a^*$ is a Jordan homomorphism of $\mathfrak{A}$ and in addition that $\mathfrak{A}$ has an identity element for which $1^* = 1$. We see that $(a \cdot 1 \cdot a)^* = (a^* \cdot 1^* \cdot a^*)$ implies

$$(24) \qquad\qquad (a^2)^* = (a^*)^2.$$

We may replace a by $(x + y)$ in (24) to obtain

$$(x^2 + x \cdot y + y \cdot x + y^2)^* = (x^* + y^*)^2$$
$$= (x^*)^2 + x^* \cdot y^* + y^* \cdot x^* + (y^*)^2$$

or $\qquad\qquad (x \cdot y + y \cdot x)^* = (x^* \cdot y^* + y^* \cdot x^*).$

The last equation may, in terms of the Jordan product of $\mathfrak{A}^+$, be written as (for characteristic $\neq 2$) $(xy)^* = x^* y^*$. Thus, the Jordan homomorphism of $\mathfrak{A}$ with $1^* = 1$ is a homomorphism of $\mathfrak{A}^+$.

Jordan homomorphisms without the restrictions we have imposed on the image of the identity have been investigated by Professor I. Herstein [12], and one may find an application of our special result to projective geometry in [8, p. 84].

5. ABSTRACT JORDAN ALGEBRAS AND THEIR LINEARIZED IDENTITIES

We have defined an abstract Jordan algebra $\mathfrak{A}$ over a field Φ to be a nonassociative algebra satisfying the identities

$$ab = ba,$$
$$(a^2 b)a = a^2(ba)$$

for all $a, b \in \mathfrak{A}$. With these as our only assumptions, simple questions must now be faced that have previously been pawned off on some special Jordan algebra $\mathfrak{B}^+$ ($\mathfrak{B}$ associative). For example, if we define a^n inductively by the equation

$$a^n = a^{n-1}a,$$

then it is not immediately obvious that

$$a^n a^m = a^{n+m}.$$

The latter equation is easily seen to be both a necessary and sufficient condition for the subalgebra of $\mathfrak{A}$ generated by a to be an associative algebra. Techniques for answering such questions must be developed.

If $\mathfrak{A}$ is a nonassociative algebra over a field Φ and x is any element of $\mathfrak{A}$, the linear transformations of $\mathfrak{A}$ into $\mathfrak{A}$ (as a vector space over Φ) defined by the equations

$$R_x: a \longrightarrow ax \quad \text{or} \quad aR_x = ax \quad \text{for all } a \in \mathfrak{A},$$

$$L_x: a \longrightarrow xa \quad \text{or} \quad aL_x = xa \quad \text{for all } a \in \mathfrak{A},$$

are called the *right* and *left multiplications* in $\mathfrak{A}$.

We note that

(25) $\quad (a\alpha)R_x = (a\alpha)x = a(\alpha x) = aR_{\alpha x} \quad \text{or} \quad \alpha R_x = R_{\alpha x},$

(26) $\quad aR_{x+y} = a(x + y) = ax + ay = aR_x + aR_y = a(R_x + R_y)$

or $\qquad\qquad\qquad\qquad R_{x+y} = R_x + R_y.$

Similar equations are valid for left multiplications.

When $\mathfrak{A}$ is an associative algebra,

(27) $\quad a(xy) = (ax)y \quad \text{implies} \quad aR_{xy} = aR_x R_y \quad \text{or} \quad R_{xy} = R_x R_J$

and

(28) $\quad (xy)a = x(ya) \quad \text{implies} \quad aL_{xy} = aL_y L_x \quad \text{or} \quad L_{xy} = L_y L_x.$

The preceding equations imply that the mapping $a \longrightarrow R_a$ is a homomorphism and the mapping $a \longrightarrow L_a$ an antihomomorphism of the associative algebra $\mathfrak{A}$ into the associative algebra $L(\mathfrak{A})$ of all linear transformations of $\mathfrak{A}$. The *representation* $a \longrightarrow R_a$ is one-to-one if $\mathfrak{A}$ has an identity element because $R_a = R_b$ implies $1R_a = 1R_b$ or $a = b$.

The representation of an associative algebra in terms of linear transformations provides an effective approach to the study of an algebra. Unfortunately if an algebra $\mathfrak{A}$ is not associative, the mapping $a \longrightarrow R_a$ is not a homomorphism. Nonetheless, the multiplications R_x, L_x will prove useful even when $\mathfrak{A}$ is nonassociative, and we denote by $E(\mathfrak{A})$ the subalgebra of $L(\mathfrak{A})$ generated by the multiplications R_x and L_x for all $x \in \mathfrak{A}$. The associative algebra $E(\mathfrak{A})$ is called the *multiplication algebra* (enveloping algebra) of $\mathfrak{A}$.

If $\mathfrak{A}$ is a Jordan algebra, the identity $ab = ba$ implies $bL_a = bR_a$ or $L_a = R_a$; hence, we may always use right multiplications when dealing with Jordan algebras. The identity $(a^2b)a = a^2(ba)$ of a Jordan algebra implies

$$(29) \qquad bL_{a^2}R_a = bR_aL_{a^2} \quad \text{or} \quad R_aR_{a^2} = R_{a^2}R_a.$$

The last equation may be written

$$(30) \qquad [R_a, R_{a^2}] = 0,$$

where $[X, Y] = X \cdot Y - Y \cdot X$ is the "commutator" multiplication in the associative algebra $E(\mathfrak{A})$.

An alternative to the linearization of the identity $(a^2b)a = a^2(ba)$ is the linearization of the identity $[R_a, R_{a^2}] = 0$ with respect to the subscripts. Thus, we replace a by $x + y + z, x + y, x + z, y + z, x, y,$ and z in turn and evaluate the second difference

$$0 = [R_{x+y+z}, R_{(x+y+z)^2}] - [R_{x+y}, R_{(x+y)^2}] - [R_{x+z}, R_{(x+z)^2}]$$
$$- [R_{y+z}, R_{(y+z)^2}] + [R_x, R_{x^2}] + [R_y, R_{y^2}] + [R_z, R_{z^2}].$$

A straightforward (but lengthy) calculation using the properties (25), (26) and the fact that the base field Φ is not of characteristic two reduces the preceding equation to

$$(31) \qquad [R_x, R_{yz}] + [R_y, R_{zx}] + [R_z, R_{xy}] = 0.$$

If we now operate on an arbitrary element b of the Jordan algebra $\mathfrak{A}$ by the transformation identity (31), we obtain the identity

$$(32) \quad (bx)(yz) + (by)(zx) + (bz)(xy)$$
$$= [b(yz)]x + [b(zx)]y + [b(xy)]z$$

for arbitrary elements b, x, y, z of a Jordan algebra.

We may set $x = y = z = a$ in (32) to obtain

$$3a^2(ba) = 3(a^2b)a,$$

so that (32) is equivalent to the original identity in a Jordan algebra if Φ is a field of characteristic not three. Henceforth, we shall assume Φ is not of characteristic two or three.

The identity (32) may be treated as multiplications acting on x and we obtain

$$xR_bR_{yz} + xR_zR_{by} + xR_yR_{zb} = xR_{b(yz)} + xR_zR_bR_y + xR_yR_bR_z;$$

or, changing notation,

$$(33) \quad R_xR_{yz} + R_yR_{zx} + R_zR_{xy} = R_{x(yz)} + R_zR_xR_y + R_yR_xR_z.$$

Another identity may be obtained by interchanging x and z in (33) and subtracting the result from (33); we obtain

$$(34) \quad R_{x(yz)} - R_{(xy)z} = R_xR_zR_y + R_yR_zR_x - R_zR_xR_y - R_yR_xR_z,$$

or

$$(35) \quad R_{x(yz)} - R_{(xy)z} = [[R_x, R_z], R_y].$$

We can now prove

THEOREM 5.1: *Every element a of a Jordan algebra generates an associative subalgebra.*

Proof: Define inductively $a^1 = a$ and $a^n = a^{n-1}a$. If we set $x = a$, $y = a^k$, $z = a$ in (33), we obtain

$$(36) \qquad R_{a^{k+2}} = R_{a^k}R_{a^2} + 2R_aR_{a^{k+1}} - R_a^2R_{a^k} - R_{a^k}R_a^2.$$

The right multiplications R_a and R_{a^2} commute as we have seen in (30). The recursive relation (36) implies that R_{a^n} is contained in the subalgebra of $E(\mathfrak{A})$ generated by R_a and R_{a^2}. Hence

$$R_{a^n}R_{a^m} = R_{a^m}R_{a^n}.$$

Let us proceed by induction to prove that

$$a^na^m = a^{n+m},$$

from which the theorem follows immediately. By definition $a^n = a^{n-1}a$, so let us assume $a^na^k = a^{n+k}$ for all n. Then

$$a^na^{k+1} = a^n(a^ka) = a^kR_aR_{a^n} = a^kR_{a^n}R_a = (a^ka^n)a$$
$$= (a^na^k)a = (a^{n+k})a = a^{n+k+1},$$

and our proof is complete.

In general, a nonassociative algebra having the property that every element a generates an associative subalgebra is called a *power associative* algebra. Jordan algebras are power associative algebras.

6. THE RADICAL, SEMISIMPLICITY, AND SIMPLICITY OF ALGEBRAS

Before we make use of the identities derived in the last section, we will take time out to discuss some general concepts of algebraic structure. Many of the ideas to be introduced apply to any class of nonassociative algebras and we will indulge in a limited amount of generality.

A nonassociative algebra $\mathfrak{A}$ over a field Φ is called *simple* if and only if

  (i) the only proper ideal of $\mathfrak{A}$ is the 0 ideal;
  (ii) $\mathfrak{A}^2 = \mathfrak{A}\mathfrak{A} \neq 0$.

We note that $(\mathfrak{A}\mathfrak{A})\mathfrak{A} \subseteq \mathfrak{A}\mathfrak{A}$ and $\mathfrak{A}(\mathfrak{A}\mathfrak{A}) \subseteq \mathfrak{A}\mathfrak{A}$ so that $\mathfrak{A}^2$ is an ideal of $\mathfrak{A}$; hence, if $\mathfrak{A}$ is simple it follows from (ii) that $\mathfrak{A}^2 = \mathfrak{A}$.

One of the main objectives in the study of any class of algebras is the determination of the simple algebras. Of course, this determination should be accompanied by some expression of the relation between a typical algebra in the class and the simple algebras. A brief account of the situation for finite-dimensional associative algebras will illustrate the points we wish to emphasize and provide the appropriate setting for comparisons.

Let $\mathfrak{A}$ be an associative algebra over Φ. An element $a \in \mathfrak{A}$ is called *nilpotent* if $a^n = 0$ for some integer n. If $\mathfrak{H}$ is an ideal in $\mathfrak{A}$, then

$$\mathfrak{H}^n = \mathfrak{H}^{n-1}\mathfrak{H} \qquad (n = 2, 3, \cdots)$$

is an ideal in $\mathfrak{A}$ and $\mathfrak{H}$ is said to be a nilpotent ideal if $\mathfrak{H}^k = 0$ for some integer k. The following observations about nilpotent algebras and ideals are stated for the convenience of future reference:

(37a)   Let $\mathfrak{H}$ be an ideal of $\mathfrak{A}$ and assume that the quotient algebra $\mathfrak{A}/\mathfrak{H}$, as well as $\mathfrak{H}$, is nilpotent. Then $\mathfrak{A}$ is nilpotent.

(37b)   If $\mathfrak{H}$ and $\mathfrak{K}$ are nilpotent ideals of $\mathfrak{A}$, then $\mathfrak{H} + \mathfrak{K}$ is a nilpotent ideal of $\mathfrak{A}$.

For the proof of (37a), let $\overline{\mathfrak{A}} \cong \mathfrak{A}/\mathfrak{H}$. The nilpotence of $\overline{\mathfrak{A}}$ means $\overline{\mathfrak{A}}^n = 0$ for some integer n and this implies $\mathfrak{A}^n \subseteq \mathfrak{H}$. Now the nilpotence of $\mathfrak{H}$ implies $(\mathfrak{A}^n)^k \subseteq \mathfrak{H}^k = 0$ for some integer k. In the proof of (37b), we make use of the second isomorphism theorem for groups,

(38) $(\mathfrak{H} + \mathfrak{K})/\mathfrak{K} \cong \mathfrak{H}/\mathfrak{H} \cap \mathfrak{K}.$

This isomorphism is applicable to the ideals $\mathfrak{H}$, $\mathfrak{K}$, and $\mathfrak{H} + \mathfrak{K}$. We note that homomorphic images and subalgebras of nilpotent ideals are nilpotent so that (37b) follows at once from (38).

For finite-dimensional associative algebras, (37) implies the existence of a unique maximal nilpotent ideal $\mathfrak{N}$ of an algebra $\mathfrak{A}$. The ideal $\mathfrak{N}$ is called the *radical* of $\mathfrak{A}$. The quotient algebra $\mathfrak{A}/\mathfrak{N}$ has zero radical and any algebra whose radical is the zero ideal is called a *semisimple* algebra. The Wedderburn structure theorems for finite-dimensional associative algebras take the form:

(39a)   If $\mathfrak{N}$ is the radical of $\mathfrak{A}$, the quotient algebra $\mathfrak{A}/\mathfrak{N}$ is a semisimple algebra.

(39b)   A semisimple algebra $\mathfrak{A}$ is the direct sum of ideals each of which is a simple algebra.

(39c)   A simple algebra $\mathfrak{A}$ is isomorphic to the algebra of linear transformations of a finite-dimensional vector space over a skew field (division ring).

If we wish to provide the class of Jordan algebras with a sequence of theorems analogous to (39), the problem of defining a suitable radical is raised immediately. We have seen that every element of a Jordan algebra generates an associative subalgebra and therefore the definition of a nilpotent element may be taken over from the associative theory without change. However, the different associations possible for a product of n elements make it necessary to alter the definition of a nilpotent algebra (or ideal) in the nonassociative case.

A nonassociative algebra $\mathfrak{A}$ is called *nilpotent* if there exists an integer n such that all possible products of n elements in $\mathfrak{A}$ are zero. For example, if n were 4, we would insist that

$$((ab)c)d = (a(bc))d = (ab)(cd) = a(b(cd)) = a((bc)d) = 0$$

for all elements $a, b, c, d \in \mathfrak{A}$.

The concept of a nilpotent ideal in a nonassociative algebra $\mathfrak{A}$ can be given an associative interpretation in terms of the multiplication algebra $E(\mathfrak{A})$ of $\mathfrak{A}$. If $\mathfrak{H}$ is a subalgebra of $\mathfrak{A}$, we denote by $\mathfrak{H}^*$ the subalgebra of $E(\mathfrak{A})$ generated by the linear transformations R_h and L_h for all $h \in \mathfrak{H}$. We note that $\mathfrak{H}^*$ and $E(\mathfrak{H})$ are not the same since they are composed of transformations on different vector spaces; however, $E(\mathfrak{A}) = \mathfrak{A}^*$. We state without proof

THEOREM 6.1: *An ideal $\mathfrak{H}$ of a nonassociative algebra $\mathfrak{A}$ is nilpotent if and only if the (associative) subalgebra $\mathfrak{H}^*$ of $E(\mathfrak{A})$ is nilpotent.*

Unfortunately, for nonassociative algebras in general (although this is not the case for Jordan algebras), the concept of nilpotent ideals given above does not lead to a satisfactory definition of a radical. The principal difficulty is that the analogue of (37a) is not valid. Albert [2], Amitsur [7], and others have discussed the concept of radicals for nonassociative algebras, and we will present here a specialization that has proved successful for Jordan algebras.

The *derived series* of a nonassociative algebra $\mathfrak{A}$ is a sequence of subalgebras of $\mathfrak{A}$ defined inductively by

$$\mathfrak{A}^{(1)} = \mathfrak{A}, \quad \mathfrak{A}^{(2)} = \mathfrak{A}^{(1)} \mathfrak{A}^{(1)} = \mathfrak{A}\mathfrak{A}, \quad \mathfrak{A}^{(i+1)} = \mathfrak{A}^{(i)} \mathfrak{A}^{(i)}.$$

An algebra $\mathfrak{A}$ is called *solvable* if $\mathfrak{A}^{(n)} = 0$ for some integer n. It should be clear that subalgebras of solvable algebras are solvable, and similarly the homomorphic images of solvable algebras are solvable. The analogues of (37) are valid for solvable ideals and there is no reason to reproduce the corresponding (and practically identical) proofs. Thus,

(40a)   If $\mathfrak{H}$ is a solvable ideal of a nonassociative algebra $\mathfrak{A}$ and the quotient algebra $\mathfrak{A}/\mathfrak{H}$ is solvable, then $\mathfrak{A}$ is solvable.

(40b)   If $\mathfrak{H}$ and $\mathfrak{K}$ are solvable ideals of an algebra $\mathfrak{A}$, then $\mathfrak{H} + \mathfrak{K}$ is a solvable ideal of $\mathfrak{A}$.

Precisely as in the associative case for nilpotent ideals, (40) implies the existence of a unique maximal solvable ideal in any finite-dimensional nonassociative algebra $\mathfrak{A}$, and we may define this ideal $\mathfrak{N}$ to be the *radical* of $\mathfrak{A}$. The quotient algebra $\mathfrak{A}/\mathfrak{N}$ has a zero radical (no solvable ideal $\neq 0$) and a Jordan algebra is semisimple if its (solvable) radical is zero.

There is no ambiguity in terminology for associative algebras between (nilpotent) radical and (solvable) radical since the concepts of nilpotent and solvable ideals are identical. However, this equivalance is not readily apparent for Jordan algebras. It is easily seen that a nilpotent ideal is solvable, but for Jordan algebras the proof that a solvable ideal is nilpotent requires justification. A proof of this fact involves the concept of a *nilalgebra*; that is, a power associative algebra in which every element is nilpotent. We shall omit proofs and merely remark that for Jordan algebras of finite dimension the concepts of nilpotent, solvable, or nilideal are all equivalent and the radical can be defined as the unique maximal solvable ideal. We then have the fact that $\mathfrak{A}/\mathfrak{N}$ is semisimple and an analogue of the first observation of (39) is valid for Jordan algebras.

7. TRACE FORMS AND SEMISIMPLE JORDAN ALGEBRAS

The second Wedderburn structure theorem of (39) for associative algebras has a Jordan algebra analogue; that is, we are able to prove

THEOREM 7.1: *Any finite-dimensional semisimple Jordan algebra* $\mathfrak{A}$ *over a field* Φ *of characteristic* 0 *is uniquely expressible as a direct sum*

$$\mathfrak{A} = \mathfrak{A}_1 \oplus \mathfrak{A}_2 \oplus \cdots \oplus \mathfrak{A}_n$$

of ideals $\mathfrak{A}_i$ *which are simple Jordan algebras.*

The restriction of the characteristic is unnecessary but the proof for arbitrary characteristic presents difficulties we wish to avoid. We shall use a "trace" argument and this will require further discussion of the right multiplications R_x, $x \in \mathfrak{A}$.

Let $\mathfrak{A}$ be a finite-dimensional Jordan algebra over a field Φ of characteristic 0. Relative to a basis $a_1, a_2, \cdots, a_n$ of $\mathfrak{A}$ (as a vector space over Φ), we note that

$$(41) \qquad a_i x = a_i R_x = \sum_{j=1}^{n} \alpha_{ij} a_j \qquad (i = 1, 2, \cdots, n),$$

where $\alpha_{ij} \in \Phi$ and the $n \times n$ matrix $[\alpha_{ij}]$ is a representation of R_x. The *trace* of the matrix $[\alpha_{ij}]$, defined by

$$\text{trace} ([\alpha_{ij}]) = \alpha_{11} + \alpha_{22} + \cdots + \alpha_{nn},$$

is the sum of the characteristic roots of R_x and is independent of the particular matrix representation. Hence we may use the notation trace (R_x) without introducing any ambiguity. We recall the following properties for the trace function [16, p. 104]:

$$\text{trace} (R_x + R_y) = \text{trace} \, R_x + \text{trace} \, R_y,$$

$$\text{trace} (\alpha R_x) = \alpha \, \text{trace} \, R_x,$$

$$(42) \qquad \text{trace} (R_x R_y) = \text{trace} (R_y R_x) \quad \text{or} \quad \text{trace} ([R_x, R_y]) = 0.$$

A symmetric bilinear form (x, y) defined on an arbitrary non-associative algebra $\mathfrak{A}$ is called an *associative form* (invariant form) if

$$(x, yz) = (xy, z)$$

holds for all $x, y, z \in \mathfrak{A}$.

An associative symmetric bilinear form is in particular an inner product defined on $\mathfrak{A}$ and we shall use that notation. For example, if $\mathfrak{H}$ is an ideal of $\mathfrak{A}$, $\mathfrak{H}^{\perp}$ will denote the set of all elements $x \in \mathfrak{A}$ such that $(h, x) = 0$ for all $h \in \mathfrak{H}$. In particular, if $a \in \mathfrak{A}$, $h \in \mathfrak{H}$, $k \in \mathfrak{H}^{\perp}$, then

$$(h, ak) = (ha, k) = (h^*, k),$$

where $h^* = ha \in \mathfrak{H}$, since $\mathfrak{H}$ is an ideal. Hence $(h, ak) = 0$ and $ak \in \mathfrak{H}^{\perp}$ for all $a \in \mathfrak{A}$. Similarly, $(h, ka) = 0$ and $ka \in \mathfrak{H}^{\perp}$. Hence the set $\mathfrak{H}^{\perp}$ is an ideal of $\mathfrak{A}$ if $\mathfrak{H}$ is an ideal.

An associative form for a Jordan algebra $\mathfrak{A}$ is provided by defining

$$(x, y) = \text{trace } R_{xy}.$$

The commutativity of $\mathfrak{A}$, the properties previously discussed for R_z, and the trace function assure us that (x, y) is a symmetric bilinear form defined on $\mathfrak{A}$. Moreover, upon taking the trace of both sides of (35),

$$R_{x(yz)} - R_{(xy)z} = [[R_x, R_z], R_y],$$

we see that an application of (42) yields

$$\text{trace } (R_{x(yz)} - R_{(xy)z}) = 0$$

or $(x, yz) = (xy, z)$. We conclude that $(x, y) = \text{trace } R_{xy}$ is an associative form for a Jordan algebra $\mathfrak{A}$.

A trace form (x, y) is said to be nondegenerate if $(x, y) = 0$ for all $x \in \mathfrak{A}$ implies $y = 0$. The importance of a nondegenerate associative form is illustrated in the following theorem.

THEOREM 7.2: *Let $\mathfrak{A}$ be a finite-dimensional nonassociative algebra satisfying the following conditions:*

(i) $\mathfrak{A}$ *has a nondegenerate associative form (x, y);*
(ii) $\mathfrak{A}$ *contains no ideal $\mathfrak{H} \neq 0$ with $\mathfrak{H}^2 = 0$.*

Then $\mathfrak{A}$ is (uniquely) expressible as a direct sum

$$\mathfrak{A} = \mathfrak{A}_1 \oplus \mathfrak{A}_2 \oplus \cdots \oplus \mathfrak{A}_n$$

of ideals $\mathfrak{A}_i$ which are simple algebras.

Proof: Let $\mathfrak{A}_1$ be a minimal nonzero ideal in $\mathfrak{A}$. Then $\mathfrak{A}_1^\perp$ is an ideal of $\mathfrak{A}$ and $\mathfrak{A}_1 \cap \mathfrak{A}_1^\perp$ is an ideal in $\mathfrak{A}_1$ so that $\mathfrak{A}_1 \cap \mathfrak{A}_1^\perp$ is either $\mathfrak{A}_1$ or 0.

In the case that $\mathfrak{A}_1 \cap \mathfrak{A}_1^\perp = \mathfrak{A}_1$, let x, y be arbitrary elements of $\mathfrak{A}_1$ and $z \in \mathfrak{A}$; then $(xy, z) = (x, yz) = 0$ because x is also contained in $\mathfrak{A}_1^\perp$ and $yz \in \mathfrak{A}_1$. Since the given form is nondegenerate, $(xy, z) = 0$ implies $xy = 0$ or $\mathfrak{A}_1^2 = 0$ contrary to (ii).

Now assume $\mathfrak{A}_1 \cap \mathfrak{A}_1^\perp = 0$. Then it follows from the general theory of bilinear forms that $\mathfrak{A} = \mathfrak{A}_1 \oplus \mathfrak{A}_1^\perp$ and the restriction of (x, y) to $\mathfrak{A}_1^\perp$ is a nondegenerate associative form for $\mathfrak{A}_1^\perp$. Moreover any ideal $\mathfrak{K}$ of $\mathfrak{A}_1^{\perp}$ is an ideal of $\mathfrak{A}$ because $\mathfrak{A}_1\mathfrak{A}_1^{\perp} = 0$. Hence $\mathfrak{A}_1^{\perp}$ satisfies the hypothesis of the theorem and we may use induction on dimension to obtain

$$\mathfrak{A}_1^{\perp} \cong \mathfrak{A}_2 \oplus \cdots \oplus \mathfrak{A}_n,$$

where $\mathfrak{A}_i$ are ideals of $\mathfrak{A}_1^{\perp}$ (or $\mathfrak{A}$) which are simple algebras. Any ideal of $\mathfrak{A}_1$ is an ideal of $\mathfrak{A}$ so that the minimality of $\mathfrak{A}_1$ implies $\mathfrak{A}_1$ is simple and our proof is complete.

In order to apply Theorem 7.2 to obtain Theorem 7.1, we only have to show that $(x, y) = \text{trace } R_{xy}$ is a nondegenerate form for a semisimple Jordan algebra $\mathfrak{A}$. Certainly a semisimple Jordan algebra $\mathfrak{A}$ contains no ideals $\mathfrak{H}$ such that $\mathfrak{H}^2 = 0$ because $\mathfrak{H}$ would then be a solvable ideal contained in the radical $\mathfrak{R} = 0$.

Let $\mathfrak{A}$ be a semisimple Jordan algebra so that $\mathfrak{A}$ contains no solvable (or nil) ideals. If every element $x \in \mathfrak{A}$ were nilpotent, then $\mathfrak{A}$ itself would be its own radical and not semisimple. Hence there is an element $x \in \mathfrak{A}$ that is not nilpotent. The element x generates an associative subalgebra of $\mathfrak{A}$, and we use the theory of associative algebras to conclude that this subalgebra contains a nonzero *idempotent* element e such that $e^2 = e$. We set $x = y = z = e$ in (33) to obtain the relation

$$(43) \qquad 2R_e^3 - 3R_e^2 + R_e = R_e(2R_e - 1)(R_e - 1) = 0$$

for any idempotent element $e \in \mathfrak{A}$. The characteristic roots of any matrix representation of R_e must be either 0, $\frac{1}{2}$, or 1. Since $e^2 = e$ implies $eR_e = e$, a nonzero idempotent e must have 1 as one of the characteristic roots of R_e. The trace of a matrix is equal to the sum of the characteristic roots and consequently trace $R_e \neq 0$ for a nonzero idempotent.

We can now prove

LEMMA 7.3: *The associative form $(x, y) = \text{trace } R_{xy}$ of a semisimple finite-dimensional Jordan algebra $\mathfrak{T}$ is nondegenerate.*

Proof: The set $\mathfrak{A}^{\perp}$ (relative to (x, y)) is an ideal in $\mathfrak{A}$. If $\mathfrak{A}^{\perp}$ contains an idempotent $e \neq 0$, then

$$\text{trace } R_e = \text{trace } R_{ee} = (e, e) \neq 0.$$

This is impossible under the hypothesis of the theorem because $e \in \mathfrak{A}^\perp$ and $(a, e) = 0$ for all $a \in \mathfrak{A}$. Hence $\mathfrak{A}^\perp$ has no nonzero idempotents and every element of $\mathfrak{A}^\perp$ must be nilpotent. Then $\mathfrak{A}^\perp$ is a nilideal (and solvable) so that $\mathfrak{A}^\perp \subseteq$ radical $= 0$. The relation $(a, x) = 0$ for all $a \in \mathfrak{A}$ implies $x \in \mathfrak{A}^\perp = 0$ so that $(x, y) =$ trace R_{xy} is nondegenerate on $\mathfrak{A}$.

The preceding lemma, when combined with the observation following Theorem 7.2, completes the proof of Theorem 7.1.

There are other illustrations of the role played by the trace form in the study of Jordan algebras over fields of characteristic 0. For example, it is possible to show that the radical of a finite-dimensional Jordan algebra is $\mathfrak{A}^\perp$ (relative to the trace form $(x, y) =$ trace R_{xy}). The trace form may also be used in proving that a semisimple Jordan algebra has an identity element. We shall accept this fact without proof since it will be necessary for our classification of the simple Jordan algebras.

8. CENTRAL SIMPLE ALGEBRAS

In order to complete the comparison of the structure of Jordan algebras and associative algebras, there remains the problem of determining the simple Jordan algebras. Our discussion will, of necessity, be largely descriptive and the next two sections will be devoted to the definition of the necessary auxiliary concepts.

The *center* $\mathfrak{Z}$ of an associative algebra $\mathfrak{A}$ consists of those elements $c \in \mathfrak{A}$ for which $ac = ca$ for all $a \in \mathfrak{A}$. If $\mathfrak{A}$ has an identity element, then $\mathfrak{Z} \supseteq \Phi$. Moreover, in the case that $\mathfrak{A}$ is a simple algebra, it can be shown that the center is a field and $\mathfrak{A}$ may be considered as an algebra over $\mathfrak{Z}$.

The *center* of a nonassociative algebra $\mathfrak{A}$ consists of those elements that not only commute but also associate with all elements of $\mathfrak{A}$; that is,

$$(44) \qquad xc = cx, \quad (xy)c = x(yc), \quad (xc)y = x(cy), \quad c(xy) = (cx)y$$

for all x, y of $\mathfrak{A}$.

The relations in (44), when expressed in terms of the right and left multiplications of $\mathfrak{A}$, imply that

$$R_c = L_c, \qquad R_c R_x = R_x R_c, \qquad L_x R_c = R_c L_x$$

for $c \in \mathfrak{Z}$, $x \in \mathfrak{A}$. If we again denote the multiplication algebra of $\mathfrak{A}$ by $E(\mathfrak{A})$ as in Sec. 5, then $c \in \mathfrak{Z}$ implies that R_c commutes with all of the elements of $E(\mathfrak{A})$. Hence R_c is contained in the centralizer of $E(\mathfrak{A})$ in the algebra $L(\mathfrak{A})$ of all linear transformations of $\mathfrak{A}$. The centralizer of $E(\mathfrak{A})$ in $L(\mathfrak{A})$ is called the *centroid* $\Gamma(\mathfrak{A})$ of $\mathfrak{A}$. The elements of $\Gamma(\mathfrak{A})$ are those linear transformations γ of $L(\mathfrak{A})$ satisfying

$$\gamma R_x = R_x \gamma, \quad \gamma L_x = L_x \gamma \qquad \text{for all } x \in \mathfrak{A};$$
or,
$$(xy)\gamma = (x\gamma)y = x(y\gamma) \qquad \text{for } x, y \in \mathfrak{A}, \gamma \in \Gamma = \Gamma(\mathfrak{A}).$$

When $\mathfrak{A}$ is a simple nonassociative algebra over Φ with an identity element, it can be shown that

(i) $\Gamma(\mathfrak{A})$ is a field,
(ii) $\Gamma(\mathfrak{A}) \cong \{R_c | c \in Z\}$,
(iii) the algebra $\mathfrak{A}$ may be considered as an algebra over $\Gamma(\mathfrak{A})$ by defining $\gamma a = a\gamma$ for $a \in \mathfrak{A}$, $\gamma \in \Gamma(\mathfrak{A})$.

The concept of the Kronecker product of two algebras permits us to make the last statement more precise. Hence we review briefly the situation for two finite-dimensional nonassociative algebras $\mathfrak{A}$ and $\mathfrak{B}$ over the same field Φ. The Kronecker product $\mathfrak{A} \otimes_\Phi \mathfrak{B}$ of $\mathfrak{A}$ and $\mathfrak{B}$ (as vector spaces over Φ) consists of the elements $\sum_{i=1}^{k} (a_i \otimes b_i)$, where $a_i \in \mathfrak{A}$, $b_i \in \mathfrak{B}$. We make $\mathfrak{A} \otimes_\Phi \mathfrak{B}$ into a nonassociative algebra over Φ by assuming that the distributive laws are valid and specifying that

$$(a_i \otimes b_i)(c_j \otimes d_j) = (a_i c_j \otimes b_i d_j),$$
$$\alpha[(a_i \otimes b_i)(c_j \otimes d_j)] = [\alpha(a_i \otimes b_i)](c_j \otimes d_j) \qquad (\alpha \in \Phi)$$

for the individual summands in the product of the typical elements $\sum_{i=1}^{r} (a_i \otimes b_i)$ and $\sum_{j=1}^{s} (c_j \otimes d_j)$ of $\mathfrak{A} \otimes_\Phi \mathfrak{B}$. If the elements $u_1, \cdots, u_n$ are a basis for $\mathfrak{A}$ over Φ and the elements $v_1, \cdots, v_m$ are a basis for $\mathfrak{B}$ over Φ, then the nm elements $u_i \otimes v_j$ form a basis for $\mathfrak{A} \otimes_\Phi \mathfrak{B}$

over Φ and every element of $\mathfrak{A} \otimes_\Phi \mathfrak{B}$ can be written uniquely as a sum $\Sigma \alpha_{ij} u_i \otimes v_j, \alpha_{ij} \in \Phi$ for $i = 1, \cdots, n; j = 1, \cdots, m$.

A special case of the Kronecker product of particular interest for us occurs when $\mathfrak{B}$ is a nonassociative algebra and $\mathfrak{A}$ is a field $\Delta \supseteq \Phi$ as in the case of the centroid of a simple algebra. Then Δ contains an identity element and the set of elements of the form $1 \otimes b, b \in \mathfrak{B}$ is a subalgebra of $\Delta \otimes_\Phi \mathfrak{B}$ isomorphic to $\mathfrak{B}$. By defining

$$\delta \Sigma_1^n (\delta_i \otimes b_i) = \Sigma_1^n (\delta\delta_i \otimes b_i),$$

we can consider $\Delta \otimes_\Phi \mathfrak{B}$ as an algebra over Δ. The algebra $\Delta \otimes_\Phi \mathfrak{B} = \mathfrak{B}_\Delta$ is called the *scalar extension* of $\mathfrak{B}$ to an algebra over Δ. In the particular case of the centroid $\Gamma(\mathfrak{A})$ of a simple nonassociative algebra $\mathfrak{A}$, we can consider $\mathfrak{A}$ as an algebra over $\Gamma(\mathfrak{A})$ by studying the scalar extension

$$\mathfrak{A}_\Gamma = \Gamma(\mathfrak{A}) \otimes_\Phi \mathfrak{A}.$$

It is not immediately obvious that the scalar extension of a Jordan algebra is a Jordan algebra. Fortunately, this is the case and we suggest that the reader provide the proof.

We define a nonassociative algebra $\mathfrak{A}$ over Φ to be *central* if the centroid $\Gamma(\mathfrak{A})$ is the base field Φ. Similarly a simple nonassociative algebra is called *central simple* if $\Gamma(\mathfrak{A}) = \Phi$, and it can be shown that any simple algebra over Φ is central simple if and only if all scalar extensions $\mathfrak{A}_\Delta = \Delta \otimes_\Phi \mathfrak{A}$ are simple. Moreover, every simple algebra $\mathfrak{A}$ over Φ is central simple when considered as an algebra over its centroid $\Gamma(\mathfrak{A})$. Hence, in a sense, the problem of simple algebras can be reduced to the study of central simple algebras. The determination of the central simple Jordan algebras will be found in Sec. 10.

9. IDEMPOTENTS AND THE PIERCE DECOMPOSITION OF A JORDAN ALGEBRA

The idempotent elements ($e^2 = e$) play a dominant role in the classification of the finite-dimensional simple associative algebras [3, chap. IV, or 17, chap. III]. A similar situation prevails for

Jordan algebras and we shall discuss briefly the ideas for idempotents needed in the classification of simple Jordan algebras. Again our attention is restricted to the case of characteristic 0.

Let e be an idempotent element in a Jordan algebra $\mathfrak{A}$. We have shown in (43) that

$$R_e(2R_e - 1)(R_e - 1) = 0,$$

so that the characteristic roots of R_e are 0, $\frac{1}{2}$, or 1. The sets defined by

$$\mathfrak{A}_i(e) = \{x | x \in \mathfrak{A}, xR_e = ix\} \qquad (i = 0, \tfrac{1}{2}, \text{ or } 1)$$

are invariant subspaces of $\mathfrak{A}$ for the linear transformations R_e. It is well known that

$$\mathfrak{A} = \mathfrak{A}_0(e) \oplus \mathfrak{A}_{1/2}(e) \oplus \mathfrak{A}_1(e)$$

as a vector space direct sum, and we shall call this decomposition the *Pierce decomposition* of $\mathfrak{A}$ relative to the idempotent e. An example will be invaluable in illustrating the results to be developed for Pierce decompositions.

Example.

Let $\mathfrak{A}$ be the 2×2 matrix algebra over Φ and consider the special Jordan algebra $\mathfrak{A}^+$. Typical elements of $\mathfrak{A}^+$ are the matrices

$$a = \begin{bmatrix} a_{11} & a_{12} \\ a_{21} & a_{22} \end{bmatrix}, \qquad b = \begin{bmatrix} b_{11} & b_{12} \\ b_{21} & b_{22} \end{bmatrix},$$

and the Jordan multiplication in $\mathfrak{A}^+$ becomes

$$ab = \frac{1}{2} \begin{bmatrix} 2a_{11}b_{11} + a_{12}b_{21} + a_{21}b_{12} & a_{12}(b_{11} + b_{22}) + (a_{11} + a_{22})b_{12} \\ a_{21}(b_{11} + b_{22}) + (a_{11} + a_{22})b_{21} & 2a_{22}b_{22} + a_{12}b_{21} + a_{21}b_{12} \end{bmatrix}.$$

The matrix $e = \begin{bmatrix} 1 & 0 \\ 0 & 0 \end{bmatrix}$ is an idempotent in $\mathfrak{A}^+$ and relative to e the subspaces $\mathfrak{A}_0(e)$, $\mathfrak{A}_{1/2}(e)$, and $\mathfrak{A}_1(e)$ are respectively the sets of matrices of the form

$$\begin{bmatrix} 0 & 0 \\ 0 & a_{22} \end{bmatrix}, \quad \begin{bmatrix} 0 & a_{12} \\ a_{21} & 0 \end{bmatrix}, \quad \begin{bmatrix} a_{11} & 0 \\ 0 & 0 \end{bmatrix}.$$

Clearly $\mathfrak{A} = \mathfrak{A}_0(e) \oplus \mathfrak{A}_{1/2}(e) \oplus \mathfrak{A}_1(e)$.

Multiplicative properties for the distinctive subspaces of a Pierce decomposition will be collected together in the following lemma.

LEMMA 9.1: *The subspaces $\mathfrak{A}_i = \mathfrak{A}_i(e)$ in a Pierce decomposition of a Jordan algebra $\mathfrak{A}$ relative to an idempotent e satisfy the following properties:*

(i) $\mathfrak{A}_1^2 \subseteq \mathfrak{A}_1;$
(ii) $\mathfrak{A}_0^2 \subseteq \mathfrak{A}_0;$
(iii) $\mathfrak{A}_1\mathfrak{A}_{1/2} \subseteq \mathfrak{A}_{1/2};$
(iv) $\mathfrak{A}_0\mathfrak{A}_{1/2} \subseteq \mathfrak{A}_{1/2};$
(v) $\mathfrak{A}_0\mathfrak{A}_1 = 0;$
(vi) $\mathfrak{A}_{1/2}^2 \subseteq \mathfrak{A}_0 + \mathfrak{A}_1.$

Proof (a sketch): Let $a \in \mathfrak{A}_i$, $b \in \mathfrak{A}_j$, where $i, j = 0, \frac{1}{2}$, or 1 so that $ae = ia$ and $be = jb$. The identity in (32) with $x = e$, $y = a$, $z = e$, and $b = b$ then becomes

$$(be)(ae) + (ab)(ee) + (be)(ae) = [b(ae)]e + [b(ee)]a + [b(ea)]e.$$

The preceding relation is equivalent to

$$[(1 - 2i)ab]e = (j - 2ij)ab.$$

Now various choices for i and j yield all of the results except (vi). For this it is necessary to use (32) with $x = a$, $y = b$, $b = e$, and $z = e$.

Note that properties (i) and (ii) imply that the subspaces $\mathfrak{A}_1(e)$ and $\mathfrak{A}_0(e)$ are Jordan subalgebras of $\mathfrak{A}$. Moreover, e is an identity element of $\mathfrak{A}_1(e)$. These observations and the properties of the lemma are clearly illustrated in our example of 2×2 matrices.

The subspace relations for the Pierce decompositions of $\mathfrak{A}$ relative to an idempotent element e have a natural generalization. Let $\mathfrak{A}$ be a Jordan algebra with an identity element that is the sum of n pairwise orthogonal idempotents; that is,

$$e_i^2 = e_i; \quad e_i e_j = 0 \ (\text{if } i \neq j); \quad e_1 + e_2 + \cdots + e_n = 1.$$

Define the subspaces $\mathfrak{A}_{ij}$ of $\mathfrak{A}$ as follows:

$$\mathfrak{A}_{ii} = \{x | x \in \mathfrak{A}, xe_i = x\} \qquad (i = 1, 2, \cdots, n),$$
$$\mathfrak{A}_{ij} = \{x | x \in \mathfrak{A}, xe_i = xe_j = \tfrac{1}{2}x\}.$$

Then it can be shown that

$$\mathfrak{A} = \sum_{i=1}^{n} \oplus \mathfrak{A}_{ii} \oplus \sum_{i<j} \oplus \mathfrak{A}_{ij}$$

is a direct sum decomposition of $\mathfrak{A}$. This decomposition is called the Pierce decomposition of $\mathfrak{A}$ relative to the set of idempotents $e_1, e_2, \cdots, e_n$. Moreover,

$$\mathfrak{A}_1(e_i) = \mathfrak{A}_{ii}, \qquad \mathfrak{A}_{1/2}(e_i) = \sum_{j \neq i} \mathfrak{A}_{ij}, \qquad \mathfrak{A}_0(e_i) = \sum_{j,k \neq i} \mathfrak{A}_{jk}.$$

The idempotent elements of a Jordan algebra $\mathfrak{A}$ are classified in terms of the Pierce decompositions of $\mathfrak{A}$ relative to idempotents as follows:

(i) An idempotent e is called a *principal idempotent* of $\mathfrak{A}$ if $\mathfrak{A}_0(e)$ contains no idempotents. This is equivalent to the statement that $\mathfrak{A}$ contains no idempotent orthogonal to e.

(ii) An idempotent is called a *primitive idempotent* of $\mathfrak{A}$ if e is the only idempotent of $\mathfrak{A}_1(e)$. This is equivalent to the statement that it is impossible to write $e = e_1 + e_2$, where e_1, e_2 are nonzero orthogonal idempotents.

(iii) An idempotent e is called *absolutely primitive* if $\mathfrak{A}_1(e) = \Phi e$; that is, $\mathfrak{A}_1(e)$ is a one-dimensional subspace of $\mathfrak{A}$. Clearly an absolutely primitive idempotent is primitive.

If $\mathfrak{A}$ is a semisimple Jordan algebra, then a principal idempotent of $\mathfrak{A}$ is the identity element of $\mathfrak{A}$.

10. SIMPLE JORDAN ALGEBRAS

A central simple Jordan algebra $\mathfrak{A}$ is called a *reduced Jordan algebra* if it has an identity element $1 = \Sigma_{i=1}^{n} e_i$, where the e_i are absolutely primitive orthogonal idempotents. The number n is called the degree of $\mathfrak{A}$. The importance of the reduced Jordan algebras is reflected in the following theorem.

THEOREM 10.1: *Let $\mathfrak{A}$ be a central simple Jordan algebra over the field Φ. If Ω is the algebraic closure of Φ, then the scalar extension $\mathfrak{A}_\Omega = \Omega \bigotimes_\Phi \mathfrak{A}$ is a reduced simple Jordan algebra.*

It can be shown that any reduced simple Jordan algebra is central simple. Hence our attention is naturally directed towards the reduced algebras over the algebraic closure Ω of the base field Φ. The structure of a central simple Jordan algebra over Φ may be determined from that of $\mathfrak{A}_\Omega$.

It is certainly possible for a Jordan algebra over Φ to be reduced without Φ being an algebraically closed field. Therefore, we shall assume at the outset only that Φ is a field of characteristic 0 and $\mathfrak{A}$ is a reduced simple Jordan algebra.

As a first step, let $\mathfrak{A}$ be a simple Jordan algebra over Φ whose identity element e is primitive. In the Pierce decomposition

$$\mathfrak{A} = \mathfrak{A}_0(e) \bigoplus \mathfrak{A}_{1/2}(e) \bigoplus \mathfrak{A}_1(e),$$

it can be shown that $\mathfrak{A}_0(e) \bigoplus \mathfrak{A}_{1/2}(e)$ is contained in the radical $\mathfrak{R} = 0$ so that $\mathfrak{A} = \mathfrak{A}_1(e)$. For a reduced algebra of degree 1, $\mathfrak{A} = \mathfrak{A}_1(e) = \Phi e$. An algebraic closure argument for arbitrary Φ would proceed as follows: If $\mathfrak{A}$ is a central simple Jordan algebra over Φ and $\mathfrak{A}_\Omega$ is a *reduced* simple algebra of degree 1, then $\mathfrak{A}_\Omega = \Omega e$ and we must have had $\mathfrak{A} = \Phi e$.

We next consider the reduced simple algebras of degree 2. Hence we are considering the case that $\mathfrak{A}$ is a reduced simple algebra over Φ; $1 = e_1 + e_2$, where e_1 and e_2 are nonzero orthogonal absolutely primitive idempotents. As an example of such a situation, we let $\mathfrak{B}_n(\Phi)$ denote the n-dimensional vector space of n-tuples $[x_1, \cdots, x_n]$ over the real field Φ and form the vector space direct sum $\mathfrak{A} = \Phi 1 \bigoplus \mathfrak{B}_n(\Phi)$. Define multiplication by

$$(\alpha 1 + [a_1, \cdots, a_n])(\beta 1 + [b_1, \cdots, b_n]) =$$
$$(\alpha\beta + [a_1, \cdots, a_n] \cdot [b_1, \cdots, b_n])1 + \alpha[b_1, \cdots, b_n] + \beta[a_1, \cdots, a_n],$$

where $\alpha, \beta \in \Phi$, $[a_1, \cdots, a_n]$, $[b_1, \cdots, b_n] \in \mathfrak{B}_n(\Phi)$ and "$\cdot$" is the usual inner product. In Example 1, Sec. 4, we pointed out that $\mathfrak{A}$ is a Jordan algebra. If we set

$$2e_1 = 1 + [1, 0, \cdots, 0], \qquad 2e_2 = 1 - [1, 0, \cdots, 0],$$

then $1 = e_1 + e_2$, $e_i^2 = e_i$, and $e_1e_2 = 0$. We leave it to the reader to verify that there are no idempotents orthogonal to e_1 and e_2; $\mathfrak{A}_{11} = \Phi e_1$, $\mathfrak{A}_{22} = \Phi e_2$; $\mathfrak{A}$ is simple if $n \geq 2$.

In this illustration we see that the degree of a reduced Jordan algebra is quite different from its dimension as an algebra. Rather than pursue the question of reduced algebras of degree 2, we merely state that, in general, we obtain the Jordan algebras of symmetric bilinear forms given in Example 1, Sec. 4, with certain restrictions. The explicit theorem is

THEOREM 10.2: *The Jordan algebra* $\mathfrak{A}$ *of dimension* $n + 1$ *over* Φ *is a reduced simple algebra of degree 2 if and only if* $\mathfrak{A}$ *is the Jordan algebra of a symmetric bilinear form* (x, y) *defined on a vector space* $\mathfrak{M}$ *over* Φ *such that:*

   (i)   *The bilinear form is nondegenerate on* $\mathfrak{M}$;
   (ii) *There exists an element* $x \in \mathfrak{M}$ *for which* $(x, x) = 1$;
   (iii) *The dimension of* $\mathfrak{M}$ *is* $n \geq 2$.

If Ω is the algebraic closure of Φ and we find that the scalar extension $\mathfrak{A}_\Omega$ is a reduced algebra of degree 2, then it is well known that the symmetric bilinear form (x, y), by a proper choice of basis, can be reduced to the usual "inner product." Consequently, our illustration is typical of all reduced Jordan algebras of degree 2 over an algebraically closed field Φ. Moreover, it can be shown that the reduced simple Jordan algebras of degree 2 are *special* Jordan algebras. These algebras are subalgebras of the algebras $\mathfrak{A}^+$, where $\mathfrak{A}$ is the Clifford algebra [8, p. 186] defined by the symmetric bilinear form (x, y) on $\mathfrak{A} = \Phi 1 \oplus \mathfrak{M}$.

The recovery of the central simple Jordan algebras over Φ from the reduced simple Jordan algebras $\mathfrak{A}_\Omega$ of degree 2 is simplified by the fact that $\mathfrak{A}_\Omega$ is of this form if and only if $\mathfrak{A}$ is the Jordan algebra of a nondegenerate symmetric bilinear form and dim $\mathfrak{A} \geq 3$.

We hasten to assure the reader that a degree-by-degree analysis of reduced simple Jordan algebras does not continue indefinitely. All reduced Jordan algebras of degree ≥ 3 have a unifying feature, and many of the necessary ideas for their description are contained in the papers of Professors Curtis and Kleinfeld in this volume. We shall begin with a description of the unifying matrix algebra and any repetition from their papers will be for the convenience of reference.

Let $\mathfrak{D}$ be a nonassociative algebra over Φ with an identity element 1. The $n \times n$ matrix algebra with elements from $\mathfrak{D}$ will be denoted by $\mathfrak{D}_n$. If the mapping $d \longrightarrow \bar{d}$ is an involution in $\mathfrak{D}$ (an antiautomorphism of order 2), then it is easy to see that the mapping

$$X = [d_{ij}] \longrightarrow [\bar{d}_{ij}]^T = X'$$

of a matrix of $\mathfrak{D}_n$ onto its "conjugate" transpose is an involution in $\mathfrak{D}_n$. We call the mapping $X \longrightarrow X'$ a *standard involution* in $\mathfrak{D}_n$.

More generally, let $T =$ diagonal $[t_1, t_2, \cdots, t_n]$ be a diagonal matrix of $\mathfrak{D}_n$ ($d_{ij} = 0$ if $i \neq j$) whose diagonal elements $d_{ii} = t_i$ satisfy the following properties:

(i) $(xy)t_i = x(yt_i), \qquad (xt_i)y = x(t_iy), \qquad (t_ix)y = t_i(xy)$
   $(i = 1, 2, \cdots, n)$ for all $x, y \in \mathfrak{D}$; that is, the t_i are in the *nucleus* of $\mathfrak{D}$.

(ii) All t_i have inverses t_i^{-1} which are also in the nucleus of $\mathfrak{D}$.

(iii) $t_i = \bar{t}_i, t_i^{-1} = (\overline{t_i^{-1}})$; that is, all t_i and t_i^{-1} are self-adjoint relative to the involution in $\mathfrak{D}$.

The mapping

$$X \longrightarrow T^{-1}X'T = \text{diagonal } [t_1, t_2, \cdots, t_n]^{-1}X' \text{ diagonal } [t_1, \cdots, t_n]$$

is an involution in $\mathfrak{D}_n$ which we shall call the *canonical involution* of $\mathfrak{D}_n$ determined by $T =$ diagonal $[t_1, \cdots, t_n]$.

Denote the set of self-adjoint elements of $\mathfrak{D}_n$ under a canonical involution by

$$H(\mathfrak{D}_n, T) = \{X | X \in \mathfrak{D}_n, X = T^{-1}X'T\}.$$

If $\mathfrak{D}$ is an associative algebra, then certainly $\mathfrak{D}_n$ is associative and $H(\mathfrak{D}_n, T)$ is a subalgebra of the special Jordan algebra $\mathfrak{D}_n^+$, where we take the Jordan product to be

(45) $XY = \frac{1}{2}\{X \cdot Y + Y \cdot X\}.$

It is conceivable that $H(\mathfrak{D}_n, T)$ could be a Jordan algebra under the Jordan product in (45) without $\mathfrak{D}$ being associative. An answer to this possibility and the fundamental role played by the algebras $H(\mathfrak{D}_n, T)$ are contained in the following theorem.

THEOREM 10.3: *Every reduced simple Jordan algebra $\mathfrak{A}$ over Φ of degree $n \geq 3$ is isomorphic to a Jordan algebra $H(\mathfrak{D}_n, T)$, where $\mathfrak{D}$ is associative if $n \geq 4$ and in any case $\mathfrak{D}$ must be an alternative algebra over Φ with an identity element 1 and an involution $d \longrightarrow \bar{d}$ such that*

(i) $d + \bar{d} \in \Phi 1$;

(ii) $d\bar{d} = Q(d)1$, where $Q(d)$ is a quadratic form defined on $\mathfrak{D}$ and the bilinear form $B(x, y) = \frac{1}{2}\{Q(x + y) - Q(x) - Q(y)\}$ is nondegenerate.

Fortunately, the alternative algebras $\mathfrak{D}$ satisfying the restrictions of the theorem are precisely the generalizations to an arbitrary field Φ of the results obtained by Professor Curtis in Theorem 5 of his paper in this volume. These will be called *composition* algebras and for convenience, we give their construction in the general setting. Let $\mathfrak{D}$ be a composition algebra over a field Φ with involution $d \longrightarrow \bar{d}$ and quadratic form $Q(d)$. Denote the vector space direct sum of $\mathfrak{D}$ and an isomorphic copy $\mathfrak{D}w$ of $\mathfrak{D}$ by

$$\mathfrak{C} = \mathfrak{D} \oplus \mathfrak{D}w.$$

The elements of $\mathfrak{C}$ are written as $x = a + bw$, where $a, b \in \mathfrak{D}$, and we define a multiplication for the elements of $\mathfrak{C}$ by selecting a nonzero element $\mu \in \Phi$ and setting

$$(a + bw)(c + dw) = (ac + \mu \bar{d}b) + (da + b\bar{c})w.$$

The involution in $\mathfrak{C}$ is given by $a + bw \longrightarrow \bar{a} - bw$ and the quadratic form for $\mathfrak{C}$ is $Q(a + bw) = \{Q(a) - \mu Q(b)\}$.

The composition algebras over a field Φ are:

(I) $\mathfrak{D} = \Phi 1$ (the field Φ itself).

(II) $\mathfrak{D} = \Phi[w]$, a two-dimensional algebra over Φ with basis 1, w, where $w^2 = \mu 1$ ($\mu \neq 0$).

(III) $\mathfrak{D} = \mathfrak{Q}$, a four-dimensional algebra over Φ constructed in the manner described from those occurring in II. These *generalized quaternion* algebras are associative but not commutative.

(IV) $\mathfrak{D} = \mathfrak{C}$, an eight-dimensional algebra over Φ constructed from the quaternion algebras of III. These algebras are called *generalized Cayley* algebras.

We can combine the list of possible composition algebras over Φ with Theorem 10.3 to obtain a classification of the reduced simple Jordan algebras over Φ of degree $n \geq 3$. If $T = $ diagonal $[t_1, \cdots, t_n]$, the possibilities for $\mathfrak{A}$ fall into four classes:

(A) $\mathfrak{D} \cong \Phi 1$. The involution of $\mathfrak{D}$ is the identity mapping and $H(\Phi_n, T)$ consists of T-symmetric matrices; that is, $X = T^{-1}X^T T$.

(B) $\mathfrak{D} \cong \Phi(w)$. The involution in $\mathfrak{D}$ is given by $a + bw \longrightarrow a - bw$ and the matrices of $H(\Phi[w]_n, T)$ are called T-Hermitian since $X = T^{-1}\overline{X}^T T$.

(C) $\mathfrak{D} \cong Q$. The elements of $H(Q_n, T)$ are T-Hermitian matrices with generalized quaternions as elements.

(D) $\mathfrak{D} \cong \mathfrak{C}$. The only possible value for n in this case is $n = 3$ since the generalized Cayley algebras are not associative. The algebras $H(\mathfrak{C}_3, T)$ will be discussed in detail in the next section.

The reduced simple Jordan algebras of classes A, B, and C are obviously special Jordan algebras because they are all subalgebras of $\mathfrak{D}_n^+$ ($\mathfrak{D}$ associative).

Our results take a simpler form if we assume that Φ is an algebraically closed field. In the first place, the composition algebras have a simpler form. For each algebra of dimension greater than one, there is an element x such that $Q(x) = 0$, and it is possible to find nonzero orthogonal idempotents e_1 and e_2 such that $e_1 + e_2 = 1$, $\mathfrak{D} = e_1\mathfrak{D} + e_2\mathfrak{D}$. A composition algebra with zero divisors (such as $e_1e_2 = 0$) is called a *split composition* algebra. There is, to within an isomorphism, one split composition algebra of dimension 2, 4, and 8 over Φ. These are (in the notation used previously):

(II) (Split case) $\mathfrak{D} \cong \Phi e_1 + \Phi e_2$; $\mathfrak{D}$ is the direct sum of two fields isomorphic to Φ.

(III) (Split case) $\mathfrak{D} \cong \Phi_2$; $\mathfrak{D}$ is the 2×2 matrix algebra over Φ.

(IV) (Split case) $\mathfrak{D}$ is the split Cayley algebra, otherwise known as *Zorn's vector-matrix algebra*. It can be described as follows:

The elements of D are the matrices

$$\begin{bmatrix} \alpha & \mathbf{a} \\ \mathbf{b} & \beta \end{bmatrix},$$

where $\alpha, \beta \in \Phi$ and $\mathbf{a} = [a_1, a_2, a_3]$, $\mathbf{b} = [b_1, b_2, b_3]$ are three-dimensional vectors over Φ. Addition is the usual matrix addition with the vectors treated as elements of the matrix. Multiplication is defined by

$$\begin{bmatrix} \alpha & \mathbf{a} \\ \mathbf{b} & \beta \end{bmatrix}\begin{bmatrix} \gamma & \mathbf{c} \\ \mathbf{d} & \delta \end{bmatrix} = \begin{bmatrix} \alpha\gamma + \mathbf{a}\cdot\mathbf{d} & \alpha\mathbf{c} + \delta\mathbf{a} - \mathbf{b}\times\mathbf{d} \\ \gamma\mathbf{b} + \beta\mathbf{d} + \mathbf{a}\times\mathbf{c} & \mathbf{b}\cdot\mathbf{c} + \beta\delta \end{bmatrix},$$

where "$\cdot$" and "$\times$" are the usual dot and cross product of vectors.

We repeat that in the case of an algebraically closed field, all of the composition algebras are split and it is possible to show that $T = \text{diagonal } [t_1, \cdots, t_n]$ may be taken to be the identity matrix I without any loss in generality. We then have the following *split* reduced simple Jordan algebras of degree $n \geq 3$ for algebraically closed fields Ω:

(A) $\mathfrak{D} \cong \Omega 1$. The $n \times n$ symmetric matrices over Ω; hence an algebra of dimension $\frac{1}{2}n(n + 1)$.

(B) $\mathfrak{D} = \Omega e_1 \oplus \Omega e_2$. We can show that $H(\mathfrak{D}_n, I)$ in this case is isomorphic to the set of all $n \times n$ matrices over Ω; hence an algebra of dimension n^2.

(C) $\mathfrak{D} = \Omega_2$ (2×2 matrices over Ω). Here we may consider $\{\Omega_2\}_n$ as $2n \times 2n$ matrices over Ω. The involution in Ω_2

extends to Ω_{2n} in such a manner that $X \longrightarrow P^{-1}X^T P$, where

$$P = \begin{bmatrix} 0 & I_{n \times n} \\ -I_{n \times n} & 0 \end{bmatrix},$$

I = the $n \times n$ identity matrix. The algebra of Hermitian matrices in this case, with $T = I$, has dimension $2n^2 - n$.

(D) This case will be discussed in Sec. 11.

Again, if we begin with an arbitrary central simple Jordan algebra $\mathfrak{A}$ over Φ, then we know that upon passing to the scalar extension $\mathfrak{A}_\Omega$ (Ω the algebraic closure of Φ) we will obtain a reduced simple Jordan algebra. When $\mathfrak{A}_\Omega$ is of degree ≥ 3, the recovery of the form of $\mathfrak{A}$ from the particular class B or C was first obtained by Professor Kalish for fields of characteristic 0. We prefer to pass over these details and refer the reader to the original papers for the classification of central simple Jordan algebras over an arbitrary field Φ.

11. THE EXCEPTIONAL SIMPLE JORDAN ALGEBRAS

The reduced simple Jordan algebras of degree 3 over Φ have been described as the self-adjoint elements $H(\mathfrak{D}_3, T)$ of $\mathfrak{D}_3$, where $\mathfrak{D}$ is a composition algebra over Φ. Except in the cases where $\mathfrak{D}$ has dimension 8 over Φ, these are special Jordan algebras. By virtue of their exceptional character, these are perhaps the most interesting of all Jordan algebras and we describe them in some detail.

Let $\mathfrak{C}$ be an eight-dimensional composition algebra over Φ (a generalized Cayley algebra) with involution $d \longrightarrow \bar{d}$. The exceptional reduced simple Jordan algebra $H(\mathfrak{C}_3, T)$ consists of the 3×3 matrices, with elements in $\mathfrak{C}$, which satisfy $X = T^{-1}X'T$. These are the matrices

$$(46) \qquad X = \begin{bmatrix} \alpha & c & t_1^{-1}t_3\bar{b} \\ t_2^{-1}t_1\bar{c} & \beta & a \\ b & t_3^{-1}t_2\bar{a} & \gamma \end{bmatrix},$$

where α, β, γ are arbitrary elements of Φ, a, b, c are arbitrary elements of $\mathbb{C}$, and t_1, t_2, t_3 are fixed nonzero elements of Φ.

Multiplication for the elements of $H(\mathbb{C}_3, T)$ is the usual Jordan product $XY = \frac{1}{2}(X \cdot Y + Y \cdot X)$ and it should be clear that the matrices

$$E_1 = \begin{bmatrix} 1 & 0 & 0 \\ 0 & 0 & 0 \\ 0 & 0 & 0 \end{bmatrix}, \qquad E_2 = \begin{bmatrix} 0 & 0 & 0 \\ 0 & 1 & 0 \\ 0 & 0 & 0 \end{bmatrix}, \qquad E_3 = \begin{bmatrix} 0 & 0 & 0 \\ 0 & 0 & 0 \\ 0 & 0 & 1 \end{bmatrix}$$

are three absolutely primitive orthogonal idempotents whose sum is the identity of $H(\mathbb{C}_3, T)$.

A straightforward computation reveals that the subspaces $\mathfrak{A}_{ij}$ of the Pierce decomposition for $H(\mathbb{C}_3, T)$, defined by the equations

$$\mathfrak{A}_{ii} = \{X | X \in H(\mathbb{C}_3, T), XE_i = X\},$$
$$\mathfrak{A}_{ij} = \{X | X \in H(\mathbb{C}_3, T), 2XE_i = X = 2XE_j\} \qquad \text{for } i \neq j$$

are the following sets of matrices:

$$\mathfrak{A}_{11} = \mathfrak{A}_1(E_1) = \Phi E_1, \quad \mathfrak{A}_{22} = \mathfrak{A}_1(E_2) = \Phi E_2, \quad \mathfrak{A}_{33} = \mathfrak{A}_1(E_3) = \Phi E_3;$$

$$\mathfrak{A}_{12} = \left\{ \begin{bmatrix} 0 & c & 0 \\ t_2^{-1} t_1 \bar{c} & 0 & 0 \\ 0 & 0 & 0 \end{bmatrix} \right\}, \qquad \mathfrak{A}_{13} = \left\{ \begin{bmatrix} 0 & 0 & t_1^{-1} t_3 \bar{b} \\ 0 & 0 & 0 \\ b & 0 & 0 \end{bmatrix} \right\},$$

$$\mathfrak{A}_{23} = \left\{ \begin{bmatrix} 0 & 0 & 0 \\ 0 & 0 & a \\ 0 & t_3^{-1} t_2 \bar{a} & 0 \end{bmatrix} \right\}.$$

Hence, we have the vector space direct sum

$$H(\mathbb{C}_3, T) = \Phi E_1 + \Phi E_2 + \Phi E_3 + \mathfrak{A}_{12} + \mathfrak{A}_{13} + \mathfrak{A}_{23}$$

of three one-dimensional and three eight-dimensional spaces over Φ. Thus $H(\mathbb{C}_3, T)$ is a 27-dimensional Jordan algebra over Φ and Albert [4] proved that any simple exceptional Jordan algebra was 27-dimensional over its center. Until 1958, when Albert [6] pointed out an error in an earlier paper by Schafer [21], it had been

thought that every exceptional simple Jordan algebra was reduced.
This is not the case and a construction is given of exceptional
Jordan division algebras in the first paper mentioned above. The
determination of all Jordan division algebras remains an unsolved
problem.

If Φ is an algebraically closed field, we can show that $H(\mathfrak{C}_3, T)$
is isomorphic to $H(\mathfrak{C}_3, I)$, where I is the identity matrix. In this
case the elements t_i of (46) are 1, and $\mathfrak{C}$ is the split Cayley algebra.
A proof that the exceptional reduced simple algebras are not
isomorphic to a subalgebra of $\mathfrak{A}^+$ ($\mathfrak{A}$ associative) requires the
consideration of only this case. Actually, one is able to prove a
more general result; namely, $H(\mathfrak{C}_3, I)$ is not the homomorphic
image of any special Jordan algebra [5].

The fact that $H(\mathfrak{C}_3, I)$ is not the homomorphic image of any
special Jordan algebra has interesting consequences. For example,
as indicated in the closing paragraph of Sec. 2, we may conclude
that special Jordan algebras satisfy identities that are not valid
for the exceptional Jordan algebras. *These identities have never
been found.*

An illustration of Jordan algebra identities other than the
defining identities is in order; hence, we define in any Jordan
algebra a *Jordan triple product,*

$$\{abc\} = (ab)c + (bc)a - (ca)b.$$

It can be shown that the identity

$$\{\{\{aba\}bc\}ba\} = \{\{aba\}b\{cba\}\}$$

is valid for both special and exceptional Jordan algebras.

The sharpest result obtained for Jordan algebra identities is that
of I. G. MacDonald [14]. He has shown that any identity involving three elements that is linear in one element must be
simultaneously valid for both special and exceptional Jordan
algebras.

It might be hoped that the proof that $H(\mathfrak{C}_3, I)$ is not the homomorphic image of $\mathfrak{J}_0^{(3)}$ would suggest additional identities for
special Jordan algebras. Unfortunately, the proof is by contradiction and the most to be said is that there is some indication that

an identity exists of degree 45. In an unpublished work, Professor J. Blattner has shown that the degree of any new identity must exceed 7. The gap between these observations is a challenge that could conceivably be closed with the aid of a high-speed computer.

12. REMARKS

The special simple Jordan algebras over an algebraically closed field fall into four classes; one of reduced degree 2 and three of reduced degree $n \geq 3$. Likewise, the simple Lie algebras over an algebraically closed field fall into four classes and five exceptional algebras. In view of the Poincaré-Birkhoff-Witt theorem that assures us that all Lie algebras are "special" and Cohn's results in Sec. 4, it is not surprising that these classes of Lie and Jordan algebras have a definite relationship. Perhaps of more interest is the fact that the exceptional Lie algebras can be related to the exceptional Jordan algebras. These relations have been investigated by Professors Chevalley, Freudenthal, Jacobson, Schafer, Springer, and others. Their investigations have led to new characterizations of the exceptional Jordan algebras, different interpretations for the new simple groups, and novel settings for the projective planes coordinated by means of Cayley algebras. The best we can do is direct the readers' attention to the bibliography to be found in the lecture notes of Professor Schafer [20].

Perhaps the most conspicuous omission in our brief discussion has been that of a representation theory comparable to its associative counterpart. This aspect, at least for the associative case, is indispensable when one does not assume that the algebras are of finite dimension. The representation theory for Jordan algebras has not been neglected, but such a discussion would require considerably more space. Therefore we direct the reader's attention to the work of Professor Jacobson [18].

The unsolved problems in the existing theory of Jordan algebras and the problems arising from the latest applications of Jordan algebras to geometry and analysis present ample challenge to the student of algebra.

BIBLIOGRAPHY

1. Albert, A. A., "On Jordan algebras of linear transformations," *Transactions of the American Mathematical Society*, Vol. 59 (1946), pp. 524–555.

2. Albert, A. A., "The radical of a nonassociative algebra," *Bulletin of the American Mathematical Society*, Vol. 48 (1942), pp. 126–136.

3. Albert, A. A., "Structure of algebras," *Colloquium Publications of the American Mathematical Society*, Vol. 24 (1939).

4. Albert, A. A., "A structure theory for Jordan algebras," *Annals of Mathematics*, Vol. 48 (1947), pp. 446–467.

5. Albert, A. A., and L. J. Paige, "On a homomorphism property of certain Jordan algebras," *Transactions of the American Mathematical Society*, Vol. 93 (1959), pp. 20–29.

6. Albert, A. A., "A construction of exceptional Jordan division algebras," *Annals of Mathematics*, Vol. 67 (1958), pp. 1–28.

7. Amitsur, S. A., "A general theory of radicals," *American Journal of Mathematics*, I Vol. 74 (1952), pp. 774–786; II Vol. 76 (1954), pp. 100–125; III Vol. 76 (1954), pp. 126–136.

8. Artin, E., *Geometric Algebra*. New York: Interscience Publications, 1957.

9. Birkhoff, G., "Universal algebras," *Proceedings of the Canadian Mathematical Congress* (1946).

10. Cohn, P. J., "Two embedding theorems for Jordan algebras," *Proceedings of the London Mathematical Society*, Vol. 9 (1959), pp. 503–524.

11. Cohn, P. J., "On homomorphic images of special Jordan algebras," *Canadian Journal of Mathematics*, Vol. 6 (1954), pp. 253–264.

12. Herstein, I. N., "Jordan homomorphisms," *Transactions of the American Mathematical Society*, Vol. 81 (1956), pp. 331–341.

13. Jordan, P., J. v. Neumann, and E. Wigner, "On the algebraic generalization of the quantum mechanical formalism," *Annals of Mathematics*, Vol. 35 (1934), pp. 29–64.

14. MacDonald, I. G., "Jordan algebras with three generators," *Proceedings of the London Mathematical Society*, Vol. 10 (1960), pp. 395–408.

15. Jacobson, N., *Lie Algebras*. New York: Interscience Publications, 1962.

16. Jacobson, N., *Lectures in Abstract Algebra*, Vol. II. Princeton: D. Van Nostrand Co., 1953.

17. Jacobson, N., "Structure of rings," *Colloquium Publications of the American Mathematical Society*, Vol. 37 (1956).

18. Jacobson, N., "Structure of alternative and Jordan bimodules," *Osaka Mathematical Journal*, Vol. 6 (1954), pp. 1–71.

19. Schafer, R. D., "Structure and representation of nonassociative algebras," *Bulletin of the American Mathematical Society*, Vol. 61 (1955), pp. 469–484.

20. Schafer, R. D., "An introduction to nonassociative algebras," Lecture Notes (Advanced Subject-Matter Institute in Algebra), Oklahoma State University, Stillwater, Okla.

21. Schafer, R. D., "The exceptional simple Jordan algebras," *American Journal of Mathematics*, Vol. 70 (1948), pp. 82–94.

INDEX

Abelian category, 47
Absolute value, 13
Affine plane, 71
Algebraic curves, 10
Algebras, 3, 108
  alternative, 112
  associative, 108
  Cayley-Dickson, 136
  central, 171
  central simple, 171
  composition, 4, 178
    determination of, 115–124
    split, 179
  cyclic, 24
  derivation, 113
  direct sum of, 149
  division, 22, 108
  enveloping, 160
  generalized Cayley, 179
    construction of, 136
  generalized quaternion, 179
  Hopf, 52
  in homological algebra, 50
  involutorial, 4
  J-, 153
  Jordan (*see* Jordan algebras)
  Lie (*see* Lie algebras)
  linear associative, 21
  multiplication, 160
  nilpotent, 164
  nonassociative, 108, 144
  normal, 22
  normed, 108
  order of, 21
  power associative, 162
  quaternion, 16, 179
  quotient, 148
  real quaternion, 16
    discovery of, 106
  semisimple, 163

Algebras (*cont.*)
  simple, 22, 162
  solvable, 164
  total matrix, 22
Alternative law, 118
Associative form, 166
Associator, 119, 127
Automorphism of algebras, 148
  of fields, 14
  of groupoids, 65

Bilinear form, 113
  nondegenerate, 114
  skew symmetric, 113
  symmetric, 113
Bilinear function, 46
Bol net, 77
Burnside's conjecture, 36

Category, 47
  abelian, 47
Cayley numbers, 108, 126, 137
Cayley table, 67
Center, 169
  of an alternative ring, 130
  of a nonassociative algebra, 169
Centroid, 170
Class field theory, 30
Coalgebra, 51
Commutator, 127
  in an associative algebra, 150
Complex number, 102
  conjugate, 104
Composition algebras, 178
  determination of, 115–124
  split, 179
Coproduct, 51
Core, 79
Curves, 10
Cyclic semi-field, 24

187

190